DEEP FEELING, DEEP HEALING:

Mind/Body Wisdom for Bodyworkers

Andy Bernay-Roman, RN, MS, LMHC, NCC, LMT

Spectrum Healing Press
Jupiter, Florida

"I know that touching was and still is and always will be the true revolution."
~Nikki Giovanni

***

"Touch is love, love is touch."
~John Lennon

ISBN 10: 0970866240
ISBN 13: 978-0-9708662-4-0

Cover artwork and design: Lynne Bernay-Roman

Edited by Janet Hubbard-Brown and Sharon Burch

Centropic Integration™ and CI™ are registered trade marks of Spectrum Healing Associates, P.A., a Florida corporation.

Please note that client names mentioned throughout this manuscript have been changed.

The author of this book does not dispense medical advice nor prescribe the use of any technique to replace treatment by a physician and/or psycho-therapist for physical or mental problems. In the event you use any of the information in this book, neither the author nor the publisher can assume any responsibility for your actions. The intent of the author is to provide general information to help you in your quest for personal growth and healing.

Table of Contents

"....Because to feel something is to be alive".
~e.e. cummings
***

"All the body senses--seeing, hearing, tasting, feeling, and smelling--are all connected to emotion. I should say emotion is connected to the senses, because the emotion is the foundation."
~Marlo Morgan
Mutant Message From Forever

***

"...feelings are the essential nature of man. They are neither good nor bad, constructive nor destructive. They are. Being natural is what is intrinsic to all of life....To block any natural process is to set in motion a force towards unification."
~Arthur Janov, Ph.D.

1

Feeling, Healing, and Touch

Touch is Emotional

Touch is not neutral. No matter how dispassionate, detached, or "scientific" you are as a bodyworker, you can't rule out your client's subjective response to being touched. People come for treatment to feel better, sometimes because they're hurting, sometimes not. Touch is a highly charged event, bound in our cells with our deepest needs for contact and intimately woven into our perception of our self in the world. As a bodyworker we will encounter that human element, like it or not. Our own body resonates with it—the solidarity, the comforting, the co-mingling of energy, the humanness.

Touch is our mother tongue, the original and only language of the body. As mammals we rely on skin contact and warmth to awaken our digestive, circulatory, and nervous systems. Kittens not licked or caressed at birth, die. Gentle touch stimulates the hormone thymopoeitin, which nurtures the budding immune system into readiness, and helps us be safe in the world as separate beings. In his groundbreaking book, ***Touching: The Human Significance of the Skin***, Ashley Montagu says: "The communications we transmit through touch constitute the most powerful means of establishing human relationships, the foundation of experience."

Touch is emotional. Although bodyworkers primarily focus on the treatment of the soft tissue of the body, they are in fact treating the whole person, and often encounter an expression of emotion and/or memories triggered by touch. The science of psychoneuroimmunology (PNI) investigates the mind/body link and offers a model that bridges the connection. Holistic treatment calls for the bodyworker to be familiar with the concepts of PNI to help understand the emotional component of his or her work in order to better facilitate positive changes that last over time.

Please remember: if you aren't a psychotherapist, don't do psychotherapy. The information in this booklet is not to make you into one, but rather into a well-informed bodyworker, who knows how to recognize the signs of pending, impending, or actual integrative emotional experiences in your clients, and when or whether to refer them to another health practitioner.   Because I now work primarily as a psychotherapist (althought I refer to myself as a mind/body psychotherapist), in my original book, ***Deep Feeling, Deep Healing: The Heart, Mind, and Soul of Getting Well***, I showcase my own brand of deep feeling body-focused psychotherapy, Centropic Integration, as a path to inner integration, becoming well, and staying well. In this booklet, ***Deep Feeling, Deep Healing: Mind/body Wisdom for Bodyworkers*** , I revise and condense the psychoneuroimmunology material, edit out most of the strictly psychotherapy focus, and zero in on areas most relevant to bodywork practitioners. So if you like to synthesize approaches of heart, mind, and body to get healthy, or help your client get there, and want to be up on the latest mind/body holistic science-based approaches, this book is for you.

Me and Mine

As part of my quest to know myself and explore my inner, deeper reality, I signed up for ten sessions Rolfing in 1969. I didn't know what I was getting into, only that cutting edge bodywork and psychotherapy practioners were doing it and raving about it. Rolfing divides the body into ten zones, which each session focused in one zone. The rolfer then unwraps, stretches, loosens, and frees up the facial bundles around muscles for the sake of restoring an "original" alignment to the body, both vertically and horizontally. Along the way both memories and feelings are naturally evoked from the tissue, partly from the sheer pain of the process and partly due to some magical reality of how the body actually stores memory. Each week, for ten weeks, I suffered through my sessions, flooded with memories and feelings both during and afterwards. Not only did I end up feeling naturally intoxicated, I also began understanding something very directly: the body IS the mind! Specifically the deeper mind. When my rolfer focused below my knees for an entire ninety minutes I had memories of being three years old and riding my tricycle in my neighborhood. 3-D memories, flashbacks, re-living. I felt again what it was like to be three and free in a big world. I recollected and re-lived my little red tricycle, the chestnut trees on my block, the wind on my face. I was there! When my rolfer "tore" at my torso, I felt deep heart pain, the hurt of when my mother left me alone in bed one night to go to a party. I smelled her perfume, I touched the softness of my down quilt, I cried. When my rolfer dug into my gut to realign psoas muscles, I experienced waves of nausea and flashed on conclusions about life I had "swallowed" inauthentically or helplessly as a child. When he realigned my back with the same taut stretching moves, I touched in with how much I'd lacked support. My point is this: There's a method to all this—the body remembers, and each significant memory is tagged with deep feeling. Each body part or segment has its own "agenda" or meaning. The mysteries of our personal unanswered questions lie dormant within, and can be tapped and unlocked.

There is no effective psychotherapy without body involvement, and there is no effective bodywork without the acknowledgement and full conscious integration of the feeling/human context.

> *"For this is the great error of our day: that the physicians separate the soul from the body"*
> Hippocrates

The Only Wisdom is Body Wisdom

The mind/body conundrum has been solved. It's all one system, not the body with some disembodied mind or spirit hovering around it, but one whole system. The psychoneuroimmunologists have discovered and isolated the neuropeptide "molecule of emotion" as a biological carrier of emotionally charged memories and information embedded throughout the human body. We each possess within us a vast fluid network of these dynamically encoded molecules that churn out non-stop images, feelings, warnings, attractions, beliefs, etc. at the speed of light from the internal library of our subconscious and even unconscious memories into the light of our everyday awareness. Some people call this holograph-generating mechanism, the MIND. The mind, it turns out, is in the body. And the good news is, that if in fact we are biological machines the way we were taught in junior high school science class, we are biological machines with a heart. A heart that feels deeply and remembers everything.

Speaking of hearts: have you heard the story of the heart-transplant recipient who months after her surgery started experiencing the memories and food cravings of her deceased heart donor? Or have you heard that they're curing warts with hypnosis? What's happening to the mind/body gap? Shrinking, that's what. Science is finally bridging the gap in ways our intuition has already been doing for years.

The deep feeling, healing paradigm is this: health and illness don't happen in a vacuum. They happen in the context of your humanity. The heart is the key to unraveling the mystery of dysfunction and disease, and body language doesn't lie.

Deep feeling therapy says: "The body follows what's in the heart and mind of a person", and that means physical ailments can be seen as primitive pantomimes of inner unconscious dramas, and specifically, stored pain. At a primitive level we put, and even hide, pain in the body, in order to protect ourselves from it. We'll fragment painful memories out of consciousness for survival's sake, which makes biological sense, but leads to problems, and can often set the stage for sickness.

The goal of deep feeling therapy is to reach the body with new information, not just reach the person's intellect with "insight". And that might involve regressing to the body's essential state of awareness, which often sits deeper and more central than a person's intellect or persona. Hurts that go in when we're three don't just go away because we get older. And when they come out into awareness organically, it's bound to look and sound like a three-year-old. Fetal pain comes out with no words at all. Inner integration is real and gutsy, and can look messy. It takes courage to heal.

The word healing shares its root with the Greek word holos, which means wholeness. To heal is to make whole. To make whole involves getting in touch with and releasing stored pain. For one thing, it takes ongoing energy to keep pain tucked away in the body, and that same energy gushes forth in abundance with each emotionally integrative experience, and thus becomes available for healing.

Accessing deep inner feelings lays out a pathway to health and recovery not because of any therapeutic school of thought, but because of biology itself.

> *"A repressed heart robs the system of vitality and sets the stage for physical disease. A feeling heart, on the other hand, supplies a wellspring for physical healing."*

Psychological insight, analysis, drugs, or even emotional catharting do not guarantee freedom from pain. Even the therapies that promise "energetic release" cannot bring about lasting change, just as superficial massage cannot alter structural defects. Feelings that exist at the very core of the mind/body system must be involved in order for permanent healing to take place. This inevitably includes pain, a central topic of this book.

Homeostasis and Pain

The mind/body system operates with a homeostatic mechanism that is set to maintain and protect the status quo. It will automatically, without conscious thought or intent, split, repress, and encapsulate painful experiences in order to keep them out of consciousness. The closer a person comes to feeling pain, the more these defenses kick in to buffer the blow, and hide the pain. Fortunately, the human system also contains hard-wired directives to integrate experience. Most people know at an instinctive level that by continuing to repress those experiences that needed to be shut out of consciousness as a child, they are hindering their advancement into adulthood. They come to therapy to undo the past, only to find themselves reliving it. But this time with full feeling. Deep feeling is the key.

Feeling Is Our Healing Destiny

I can't impress upon you enough the importance of a holistic approach to health, and that being in touch with feelings, the crux of what it is to be human, is the key to getting and staying well. Neither disease nor health occur in an impersonal vacuum, but rather are brewed in the cauldron of our personhood. Our thoughts and feelings play a decisive role in our manifest destiny. The feeling heart alone unlocks this proper destiny.

Our True Nature: Nature!

To be aligned with nature is to be healthy. Mind/body science now tells us that an inner state of congruence stands central to our well-being. In their book, **Remarkable Recovery**, Caryle Barasch and Marc Ian Hirschberg report countless stories verifying the fact that a common theme for those occurrences of sponteaous healings we read about is a state of realignment with being real, being true to the core of oneself.

What keeps us from being real and sets us drifting away from a core sense of integrity or wholeness is pain. More specifically, it is our defenses against pain that shut us off from feeling, and thus from our connection to our core. Core therapy helps in the process of reclaiming our essential real nature. Reaching through our pain becomes the path of reconnecting with essence.

Our brain's tri-fold nature, a product of eons of evolution, leaves us with three brains, each with its own specific ways of organizing information, storing memory, and responding to pain. Any path towards wholeness, including bodywork, must deal with this triune nature of man, otherwise the core remains untouched. This book focuses on practical methods of accessing these three-brain aspects of our being for the sake of becoming whole and true to our core once more.

<u>Psychosemantics</u>

When I was a young man and in the enchantment of a new love, a challenging moment impressed upon me the absolute reality of how the words we use with one another can render a direct response in the physical body. When emotions run high, the effect can be dramatic.

I met long-haired, dreamy-eyed Leah at a housewarming party I was throwing to celebrate the purchase of my new home. She had tagged along to the party with a hospital co-worker friend of mine who introduced us. Leah handed me a bouquet of irises, and said in a sincere tone, " Thanks for having me at your party, and congratulations on your new home." No one had ever given me flowers before. I fell in love with her on the spot. Before the evening festivities were over I asked Leah if she'd like to get together for lunch the next day.

"Sure. Come over to my place and I'll make you pesto and hand-made buckwheat noodles." We ended up spending the day together, and the next day, too. We talked freely, laughed a lot, and melted into a comfortable fit. That weekend we went camping and set up our tent next to a waterfall an hour north of town, and that night we snuggled. The glow of our feelings kept us as warm as the fire.

As the weeks went by, Leah and I spent more and more time together, and I really felt like we were in the process of becoming an "item," but something was lacking inside me. I couldn't tell if Leah's feelings were the same as mine. Did she just like my company in a platonic way, without any desire to be in relationship?

One evening as we sat by my fireplace, Leah started getting up to go home, and I really wanted her to stay. "Leah," I said with all the passion of my desire, "I want you to know I really like you. I want us to be in a relationship. I really want something to break open at a heart level between us." Leah hugged me and mumbled something before leaving, without directly addressing my gush of feelings. I felt raw and open and yearning.

At three a.m. I awoke with dull and constant chest pains, and a layman's bout of denial. It's just indigestion, I rationalized. At 6 a.m. my pain was at a holding level of 3 on a scale of 1-10. I went to work anyway. Finally, just before lunch, when my chest pain spontaneously reached a level "5," I confided my condition to one of my fellow ICU nurses.

"Don't be a fool, Andy! You're in the ICU! What better place to be checked out." She took my hand and escorted me down to the "cath" lab to get a 12-lead EKG, and to be checked by the resident cardiologist. They took my blood to see if I had elevated cardiac enzymes, and even gave me a thallium stress test, monitoring my heart while I ran a treadmill. In the meantime, after looking over my EKG, the cardiologist called to prepare the catheterization room, and put the OR on notice. I quietly freaked out.

My enzyme test came back negative, so although my EKG showed some irregularity, they ruled out a heart attack. That's when they threw in a MUGA scan just to get a picture of my heart muscle in action. My true condition revealed itself.

"Andy, this is strange," the cardiologist said, viewing the films of my heart muscle contracting in bright red and green contrasting images before him. "Look closely at this." He pointed to a section just above the mitral valve. "See that little appendage flapping in the wind? It seems that a few strands of the tiny tendons that support your mitral valve broke loose, probably around the time you woke up in the middle of the night. Somebody been plucking at your heart strings?" he added light-heartedly.

I'm convinced my feelings of unrequited love and my declaration of "wanting something to break open at a heart level" translated from emotion to physical reality that night. The next time I saw Leah, I felt the chest pain again, elevating from a level "2" to about a "4." Leah didn't want me the way I wanted her, and that hurt--physically.

I eventually got over her, and my heart mended.   Ever since, I've been very careful about how I phrase my expressions of love.   I make sure there are no destructive implications. You can't be too careful when it comes to the mind/body connection!

Feeling and the Healing System

"I want you to go into my patient's room. Don't look at her chart or anything, and then tell me what body system is causing trouble." This was a colleague's challenge to me one slow evening in the Intensive Care Unit of the hospital where I worked. A good ICU nurse, just by paying attention to clues in speech and attitude for a few minutes, can pinpoint whether a patient's physical problems are gastrointestinal, cardiovascular, or neurological. No sweat.

"Let's see. This person is really really nice. She would have allowed me to do any test on her without asking what it was. She focused on me, and made me feel good. This person had cancer surgery, right?" BINGO! ICU nurses, by raw exposure to people, know that certain personality types seem to match certain diseases, or that certain personality types tend to be associated with various body systems. Science hasn't yet narrowed it down to specifics in determining which personalities go with what system, but Louise Hay, author of **You Can Heal Your Life**, a pioneer in this field, has done a phenomenal job of creating a map. The link between illness and personality is a major breakthrough in how we look at disease and treatment. Can every illness have a psychosomatic component to it? Can every illness therefore benefit from a particular attitudinal treatment plan?

Though common threads become apparent when reading the stories of spontaneous remission, there is no single or simple formula. The path to healing unfolds as uniquely as the history that leads up to the disease. What stands out most in healing anecdotes is the part the mind and emotions play in both the development and course of the disease, and in the healing as well. The body follows what is in the heart and mind in both illness and in cure.

Doctors today postulate that the body contains an inherent healing system far beyond the sole workings of the immune system. This healing blueprint uses information from every sub-system, and maintains connection and communication via the nervous system and the hormonal system--feedback mediated by the patient's feelings and inner images. What we are experiencing, including our thoughts and emotions, influences our health directly. How we construct our world experientially, i.e., how we process the information of each moment, what we make of each event and experience, directly influences the effectiveness of the healing system. If the body follows what is in the heart and the mind, then we potentially carry the most potent of medicines (and the most potent of poisons) around within us. Science affirms this. When our emotions trigger a cascade of brain endorphins, the natural pain killers that yield a sense of well-being, the end result is a calm, life-affirming one. When our emotions consistently trigger the release of stress hormones, designed to keep our system alert in times of emergency, the net result is life-negating and sets the stage for disease. Our emotional tone directly influences the sum total of all biochemical processes.

Scientists have found that the physical unit of memory, the messenger molecule called the neuropeptide, harbors a biochemical code (an imprinted version of every physical, emotional, and mental response we've ever had) that is linked to a vast network of receptor sites that exist on cell walls throughout the tissue of the body. All day this network of shifting molecules tirelessly responds to electrochemical triggers via the nervous and hormonal systems, touching and mediating every single biochemical process within the body, all the while generating an inner "map" out of our impressions that is designed to help us make sense of our experience and get our needs met. When asleep, our senses are withdrawn from the outside world, and we lay immersed in virtual reality. We call that "nocturnal map" a dream. Our responses to those inner-generated images are as real as the ones to outer objects or events. What makes us think that just because our eyes are open during the day that we're not generating hologramic versions of what's occurring? We are awake and dreaming, each one of us in every moment generating our unique inner version of the world, each using the palate of sensory engagement and past memory to paint our unique version of "reality".

In the waking state we call this map the mind. Some elements of this map potentially set the stage for disruptive life-negating disease processes, and some elements help us get well. Either way, the mind, as a by-product of neuropeptide activity, directly influences the central integrity of the physical system.

So what's the formula? Are positive thinking, "good" emotions, and relaxing imagery (the holy trinity of the relaxation response) the cure? Unfortunately, it isn't that simple, because the mind, as a self-fulfilling structure within which bodily reality flows, is not changed by conscious mental effort alone. It takes immersion into deep feelings to crack open our old maps and break the hold of outdated, unhealthy systems of belief. Deep feelings, reflecting a state of whole-brain operation, serve as the integrative forces within the body that set the stage for healing. This is the foundation of deep feeling therapy. Positive thinking and emotions, as well as relaxing im-agery, naturally follow in the wake of deep feeling exploration, but without it, they do not carry the necessary life-force to overcome disease.

What exactly is the difference in meaning between belief and truth, and which should we work with in our efforts to further healing? You might philosophically answer that beliefs aren't necessarily true, and therefore aren't worth looking at. Or you might say that beliefs are merely a form of subjective truth and therefore not as potent as THE truth. These subtle interpretations don't exist in the body, however, for it responds to beliefs as though they are truth. Beliefs are the body's truth, which means they are crucial to the healing system. Some beliefs further and some hin-der healing.

It Just Takes Practice

A large number of people were tested for their ability to throw basketball free- throw shots, and then they were divided into three subgroups to be measured again in three months' time. One section practiced free-throw shooting every day for one half hour. Another had nothing to do with basketball for the entire time. The third division sat quietly each day for half an hour imagining themselves practicing free-throw shots. The results showed the two groups that either practiced in actuality or in imagination both significantly improved over the group that did nothing. In changing our inner reality we directly influence results in the outer physical world.

Deep Feeling: the Good, the Bad, the Ugly

*"And here am I, patiently squeezing four dimensional ideas
into a two-dimensional stage."*
e.e.cummings

The feeling dimension is what makes us human. Unlike Sigmund Freud's notion that the deep recesses of the Unconscious contain a myriad of anti-social, unacceptable demons, what I have discovered beneath the layers of the persona looks more like repressed kid stuff, which, when appropriately evoked and raised into consciousness, can become the most potent of inner resources. It's good stuff. Very good stuff. Suffering is the result of not feeling.

"I'm so glad I can feel!" one of my teary-eyed clients said after a wrenching bout of sobbing. "It makes sense to me now. All my anxiety was nothing more than tears trying to surface, and now they're here. Thank God!" Feeling, even feeling "bad," affirms the aliveness of the heart. Few people realize that acknowledged "uncomfortable" or painful feelings are a gateway to a depth not otherwise easily accessed. The fight against depression, for instance, often causes it to persist, whereas a non-resistant descent into pain is the shortest path to relief.

We expend a lot of energy avoiding pain, dispelling it, squelching it, hiding it, and killing it. The human body produces its own natural endorphin pain-killers, as do all vertebrates on the planet. Pain repression has endured over millennia because of its vital role to survival. Nonetheless, after years of working with critically ill people, in Intensive Care units, alternative healing centers, and hospices, I'm convinced that repressed pain lies at the root of disease. I'm also convinced that removing the blocks to feeling, and then integrating the pain, marks the most direct route to re-establishing the biological grounds for healing in the body. These so-called "invisible factors" of thought and feeling are key to influencing the physical condition.

The first rule is to stop denying that the pain exists. Stop pretending, and get real. Over and over in newly formed support groups, sessions that start out as chatty and superficial soon travel deeper towards a feeling core, delving into expressions of genuine loss, caring, and despair. The same is true of one-on-one therapy. The urge to be whole, to be real, and to feel, like a dormant seed thirsting for water, creates its own momentum, and once initiated, hopefully carries the patient into the realm of health.

When a psychologist told me years ago that "the Unconscious is dangerous, leave it alone," it sounded like demonology to me. The Unconscious contains all the information we've hidden from our awareness, not only the destructive, negative feelings, but also the more tender and vulnerable feelings of need and affection. Stuffing those feelings prevents growth. Only when repressed feelings surface do their positive aspects manifest and take their place as living parts of our psyche.

The Biology of Emotional Integration

I call my work Centropic Integration™. Centropic means "natural movement towards the center". Presented with a safe atmosphere and an attentive listener who encourages self-reflection, patients naturally begin to go within, a process I call the centropic journey™. Repressed feelings emerge along the way. I discovered this healing sequence and process of inner release when working with ICU patients whose life-threatening encounters with illness shocked them into a natural regression that often facilitated a healing. I concluded that the body WANTS to integrate at the feeling level.

I learned during the process that old non-integrated feelings dominate the feeling landscape because they NEED to be integrated. They continue to color everything in the present and influence every interaction. Repressed pain robs us of our capacity for joy. Repressed sadness and anger transform into depression or some other form of inner isolation.

Jens

Jens, a lanky, childishly blond-haired 73-year-old man of Swedish descent, found himself in my ICU after years of being a smoker and ongoing bouts with emphysema. His lungs had deteriorated in recent months, and he was so short of breath that he needed IV and respiratory support just short of being hooked to a ventilator. Jens was in shock.

"I just can't believe I'm really here. People warned me and I just never believed it could happen to me." He spiraled into a depression. One evening I entered Jen's room to find him crying. I assumed his tears were his feelings of overwhelm at the worsening of his condition finally catching up with him and surpassing his many years of successful denial. I was right, but even more than I knew.

"Poor Alex," he kept repeating with tear-filled eyes.

"Who's Alex?" I asked.

"Alex is my dog. He's my best friend." Jens cooed in a voice uninhibited and soft---like that of a young boy.

"Tell me about Alex," I said, sitting at the bedside.

"I've had Alex since he was a little puppy. I found him. Father said I couldn't keep him, but Mother said it was OK. He's my best friend." More tears.

"What's happened to Alex?" I ask.

"We're out for a walk, right by our house, and I'm watching Alex run---he's a happy dog. I see him run past the curb, into the street. I see him get hit by the car. I hear the loud bump and I hear his wild yelp of pain. I run over to him. He's twitching and blood is coming out of his nose and ears." Jen's tears are flowing over his cheeks.

"Don't die, Alex, don't die. You're my best friend." Jens moans and rocks, propped up by his pillows in bed, as if he's rocking the dog in his lap.

"I can't save him. Why can't I save him? He's my friend." Finally, Jens drifts off to sleep.

Although there's a great parallel between his helpless feelings at the death of his dog many years ago (it turns out this happened when Jens was eleven), and his current situation, his tears were not symbolic or metaphorical. He was really crying for his loss of his puppy sixty-two years ago! Jen's style as a person had been one of stoicism and denial, and it took the severity and surprise of being in the ICU to break through an iron wall of defenses to his own feelings. When he did, the feelings rushed forward into consciousness as intact as the day he first repressed them!

I began to see how the hidden dynamics of feeling memory storage directly influence life dramas in the present.

Later, Jens talked with me about his experience. "I could never feel my feelings in my house. My father just said 'good riddance' about Alex. He had no sympathy for me, and even my mother down-played my sense of loss. I think she was trying to protect me. There was no one there for me, so I've hidden it all. I guess I just can't do that any more--even if I try, it seems!"

Jens navigated the flare-up of old feelings in a positive way. He softened and opened to them and to others around him. He let his family's caring penetrate his stoic shell. Funny how allowing oneself to feel pain halts suffering.

Not everyone embraces emerging feelings in such a self-transforming way. When feelings arise initially as tension or nervousness, people tend to escalate the level of defense or distraction to match the rising tide. I have often seen patients lash out at the care giver or family as a way of coping with their fears. Dr. Elizabeth Kubler-Ross identified anger as a normal manifestation of the death and dying/grieving process. Nevertheless, it remains a defense, thus overshadowing a deeper process of integration demanding to happen.

Our first inclination as care givers may be to try to make patients feel better, to cheer them up in the face of their emerging pain, but this goes against the biology of integration. Painful memories enter consciousness in order to be integrated, to relieve the mind/body system of the burden of inner secrets. Non-integrated experiences remain encapsulated in body tissue (my guess is somewhere near the neuropeptide receptor site intended for healthy memory storage), waiting to reveal themselves and be fully absorbed into ongoing reality. When we resist these emergent feelings, either through repression or distraction, they persist in their mounting urgency to release. Ironically, by allowing these fragments from the past to be integrated into the present, they lose their hold on us, and we no longer unconsciously act them out or attract their negativity. Repressed feelings become "shit magnets," and answer the question, "Why is this happening to me again?"

Jens experienced the biology of integration, a process compelled and directed by natural forces. Any therapy that goes against the tide of these biological currents of emergent feeling fragments from the past misses the true thrust of healing, and can even impede it. In being present for Jens therapeutically, it was also important for me to stay out of his way.

This is where the power of bodywork shines. Because of its direct contact and "assault" on the neuromuscular defenses against stored pain, bodywork sometimes elicits an emotional response and/or painful memories in clients because it can directly trigger neuropeptide sites and bring imprinted experiences into consciousness.

For all the irrationality that surrounds feelings, they still make sense. Rooted in the biology of need, feelings extend outward from the human heart to touch the world in a way that says "yes". Even with the most flagrantly hallucinating schizophrenics I have encountered, who spoke in seeming riddles, the feelings at the core of those expressions were completely understandable, deeply encrypted though they were within the code of their own loose-knit defense system.

I have worked with an incredibly diverse group of people, including astronauts, movie stars, artists, call girls, blue collar workers, and geniuses--and what they all share is heart. At the human need level, we stand naked together. The ignored heart remains at the core of disease, and the reclaimed heart remains at the core of healing. With all the 12-step recovery programs now in effect, has anyone focused on the recovery of the heart?

There is a trend afoot, espoused by the rational-emotive school of therapy, with the premise that irrational thinking lies at the root of our suffering, and therefore simply by changing our thoughts we can make ourselves be happy. Even this approach can have heart, because gentler, non-crisis thinking emerges from the heart-space. Positive thinking is the flowers, and the heart is the vase. Presenting someone with flowers calls for them to bring forth an appropriate container. Mental re-framing, although purely cognitive, can still issue an appeal to the heart to come alive and embrace life. On the other hand, positive thinking or affirmations, done to repress painful feelings, become agents of suffering.

Internalized Stressors: Who Needs Therapy?

With the introduction of the phrase "stress reduction" in the 1970s, and with the subsequent incorporation of that expression into our language by the 1980s, it has become all too apparent that reducing external stress factors in our lives is a good idea when creating strategies for better living. We generally seek out stress-free places for vacation, and we pace ourselves in job, home, relationships, childcare, and leisure, with the intention of staying out of the dreaded burn-out stress zone.

Science reports over the past decade link lifestyle stress with diminished immune response, accelerated tumor growth, and decreased absorption of nutrients. But what about stress responses that seem to be independent of external circumstances, such as upsets and interpersonal discord that occur even when we're on vacation and at our most relaxed? And what about stress responses like panic attacks or negative "self-talk" that occur when we're alone, and seem to be self-induced?

To the body, stress is stress, whether it is externally or internally generated. As a therapist, I am more interested in the internally-generated stressors, because they pollute the inner landscape of well-being and consistently result in making the outer world a trigger for unhappiness. Outer stressors we can avoid, but we carry inner stressors wherever we go. How stressed out a person gets in any circumstance reflects a combination of subjective and objective factors.

Based on a psychoneuroimmunology-based principle that what's out there goes in, and what's in there comes out again (that is: how learned behavior becomes a map for future interaction), internally generated stressors originate externally, and then are internalized. And just as external stressors can be eliminated by external changes, internalized stressors can be eliminated by internal changes. Deep-feeling therapy seeks to uproot these internalized sources of "poison." Good weeding requires pulling every weed, root and all.

An external event becomes an internalized or imprinted one when the body's response ingrains itself in the emotional memory of the person. From an anatomical point of view, emotions play the role of a tagging mechanism, flagging any experiences that need to be stored in memory with a high charge. Emotions associated with painful events help keep the body alert for similar threat or harm. In the case of positive experiences, emotions trigger and ingrain in memory an endorphin response to reinforce pleasurable or need-fulfilling experiences. Emotions provide a gut-level recognition of what is good and bad, what is to be avoided and what is to be sought out.

Anthony Robbins, self-help and personal transformation guru, suggests that people base their actions more on the avoidance of pain than on the pursuit of pleasure. Rather than being ruled by the Pleasure Principle of the Id, or the Reality Principle of the Ego, as Freud maintained, I believe we are ruled by the Avoidance-of-Pain Principle of the Body. Because painful experiences are tagged for self-protection by being stored with a high emotional charge in the memory system, and because pain must be avoided, conflicting forces of store it vs. stay away from it are resolved by the innate ability of the organism to do both at once The memory splits into fragments--literally. We are responding to stress in the present through fragmented memory circuits. For an incest survivor, for example, sexual encounters or even ordinary sexual feelings can trigger the emergency body-response from yesteryear and render an essentially harmless event a catastrophe. Stored pain robs us of joy.

The central approach in therapy, therefore, must be to take pain out of storage, even if it hurts. We are led to believe from recent scientific articles that emotional memory cannot be erased, only re-framed. But keeping pain in storage, that is, repressed from consciousness, keeps the re-framing process from happening. The only way to make a ceramic vase is to first put the lump of clay onto the potter's wheel. It serves no purpose sitting in the bin. Dealing with trauma only cognitively is the equivalent of discussing the theory and origins of clay without digging into the clay bin. Intellectual discussion cannot produce a real vessel. Talk therapy alone cannot heal real wounds.

Uprooting internalized pain means reversing the body's own mechanism of imprinting, by tracking down and eliciting the initial elements of trauma before they were fragmented by a survival response. Contained within pain is the magnet that draws the splintered memory bits together, and ultimately, the glue that reconnects them.

To feel childhood pain in its original format neutralizes the organismic "need" to avoid situations or persons that evoke that pain. Very simple logic, no? Feeling childhood painful experiences doesn't necessarily mean regressing to childhood, because the fact is that a non-integrated, repressed childhood memory rarely feels like something that happened long ago. It just never went away. It would more than likely feel like current reality, because it has become so deeply woven into the fabric of our adult experience that it may not even be recognizable as childhood pain any longer. But childhood pain it is, nonetheless. I haven't met anyone yet who has not carried some pain from the past into the present, and who also hasn't lost some degree of pristine enjoyment of the present because of it. Once that pain is revealed, all the associated conclusions about self and reality are loosened, and the possibility for joy reemerges.

In that regard everyone needs therapy. Like a hairy dog picking up unwanted burrs and thorns in a field of brambles, we, too, just from being in a world of human interactions, inevitably pick up and carry within our psyche inhibiting notions about what is real and true that prevent us from fully responding to the moment. Therapy serves as a thorough "comb-out" of limiting beliefs, from the superficial to those more deeply entangled in our intimate sense of self.

The knotted hair of the dog has to be cut, which will initially leave the dog's coat scraggly and irregular, but in the long run cutting out the burrs will bring out the creature's innate beauty. Hopefully, the stigma that used to be attached to therapy and counseling are gone for good, so that all of us can shine.

Why Body-Focused Psychotherapy?

Reflecting the growing mind/body interface that exists between medicine, bodywork, and psychology, body-focused psychotherapy emerges as a new approach, using the tools and wisdom of all three. Quite simply, it combines physical and psychological processes conjointly for therapeutic purposes. Although psychotherapists are technically more concerned with the wholeness of the psyche, and not the body, direct hands-on contact or body-awareness techniques often further psychological process. Despite the taboo on touching in mainstream psychology, I am convinced that appropriate and well-timed use of touch enhances the transference process, quickens inner processing, and provides corrective emotional experiences. My reasoning is based on the simple principle that because the body's physiological response is central to a person's overall response to trauma, so too must the body be involved in the therapeutic healing of such trauma---something that "talk therapy" alone cannot adequately address.

Because of the paradigm-shifting breakthrough work of psycho-immunologists like Candace Pert, Ph.D., this interdisciplinary approach to therapy has been raised a few notches above the esoteric pseudo-science realm it used to be relegated to, and directly into the rational world of clini-cal and experimental understanding. The psychoneuroimmunology move-ment, although still in its scientific infancy, has conclusively demonstrated the existence within the body of an intricate messenger molecule network that binds the nervous system, including the brain, the endocrine system, and the immune system into a single, fluid, emotion-modulated entity. The peptide molecules of emotion serve as biological mediators, not only of all the biochemical processes, but also of all human experiences. The mind, as it turns out, resides in the body, and is not localized to the brain.

Ever since Renee Descartes, the philosopher central to 17th Century Europe's scientific awakening, negotiated his turf deal with the Church to separate soul from body (he agreed that science would not challenge the notion of the Divine), these two aspects of the human be-ing have been pushing to reunite. The same is happening in the world of psychotherapy. The movement to re-somatize, or re-embody, the mind, initially started with Wilheim Reich's psychodynamic model of the early 20th Century. Reichian therapists see the body's musculature as mirroring psychological defense mechanisms. Repeated protective muscular contractions in the face of emotional trauma freeze the body/mind system into what Reich called "body and character armoring". His approach to healing involved direct hands-on contact with the supine cli-ent, deep breathing, and abreaction that all combine to simultaneously loosen both sets of armor. Today, this body-oriented approach finds ratio-nale and support from within such diverse fields as neurology, acupunc-ture and Oriental medicine, as well as major schools of psychotherapy.

Some body-oriented psychotherapies may dispense with hands-on contact and instead may focus on reflecting the client's awareness to posture or movement in order to personalize psychological insight. All embrace the notion of internalized blocked physical energy that produces tension and anxiety, thus blocking awareness. The goal of body-oriented psychotherapy is the gradual unraveling and direct release of both physical and psychological aspects of these life-negating barriers, a healthy integration of the past into the present, and a return to the normal uninhibited state.

Transformation-oriented Bodywork

Examples of body-oriented psychotherapy include: Somatic Trauma Therapy™ as practiced by Babette Rothchild of Denmark, the neo-Reichian Radix™ therapy as presented by Dr. Charles Kelley, Systemic Integration™ by R. Cascone, Ron Kurtz' Hakomi™ therapy, the Pesso Boyden System Psychomotor™ (PBSP), and Centropic Integration™ of Dr. Camden Clay and me. Other modalities in this category include: Feldenkrais™ movement-oriented therapy, Rubenfeld Synergy™, Hellerwork™, the Transformational Bodywork™ of Fred and Cheryl Mitouer, and Interactive Facilitation™.

Transformation-oriented bodywork stands as the counterpart of body-focused psychotherapy within the field of therapeutic touching, and includes those modalities of touch-oriented healing which deal with the whole of a person's experience, yet do not qualify as psychotherapies.

Ida Rolf's system (Rolfing™) of structural integration and realignment of body posture via a physical manipulation of the fascial sheets surrounding muscle bundles, stands as the grandmother of transformation-oriented bodywork. Rolf introduced her methods at the Esalen Institute of Big Sur, California, in the 1960s, which greatly helped somatosize the psychotherapy movement then. Fritz Perls, founder of Gestalt Therapy, became involved in Ida Rolf's early work at Esalen, and claimed her rolfing "saved my life." Unlike its psychotherapy counterparts, transformation-oriented bodywork often does not focus on the verbal or emotional content of the client's experience, but rather lets those elements naturally re-integrate in the wake of the physical realignment and dismantling of the body's armor.

Body-focused Psychotherapy and the Trance State

Body-focused psychotherapy aims to achieve wholeness of the body/mind system by facilitating physical, emotional, and mental changes. The work involves both physical contact with soft tissue and verbal emotional processing. This kind of psychotherapy capitalizes on a normal body/mind reality to evoke therapeutic change in a way that captures the directness and immediacy of experience itself. That reality is the trance state, a narrowing of focus to one thing wherein all else recedes into the background of our attention. It provides a kind of meditative relaxation, which buffers out pain and affords the body an opportunity to heal. This "hypnosis," as a direct corollary of the relaxation response itself, presents itself as an oasis in the vast world of busy experiences. Outside of therapy, humans seek it out over and over again in order to disengage from and ultimately stop the conscious mind from reporting lower levels of repressed pain.

Besides its pain-blocking function, our brain seeks out the trance state because it minimizes effort and awareness, and keeps us functioning smoothly. Running on auto-pilot performing familiar tasks such as driving is a good example of trance-living. Auto-pilot kicks in when we watch movies or TV. It helps us relax by narrowing our focus and disengaging fom integrative processing. A trance state contains all the soothing elements of sleep, including the deeper brain wave rhythms. Early trance states, perhaps when we were rocked as babies, or maybe even further back when we were floating in the womb, surrounded with the oceanic sounds of blood flow and heart beat, get imprinted in the mind/body system as most desireable. Trance is the mind's version of peace. We seek it out as a return to "the good old days". When a person carries repressed painful feelings, trance-inducing mechanisms must cut off inner connectedness to achieve the desired serenity. The trance then becomes at the expense of wholeness. We veg out and live unconsciously in a trance state seemingly to enjoy peace, but organismically, to avoid pain.

In body-focused psychotherapy, the therapist introduces attention to bodily reality in the immediate moment as a way of accessing which trance state the client relies on in order to maintain her repressed status quo. Trance induction is one of the body/mind's most primitive and common defense mechanisms against pain, therefore emerging as the single most potent gateway for real change. No intellectual overlay, no amount of insight or affirmations can make for lasting change, until the trance state and the feelings hidden there are addressed. Inevitably, a trance state used as a defense against pain will simply usurp all intellectual attempts to "understand" and ameliorate it. Knowing about one's history of being unloved doesn't in itself change anything.

Ironically, the trance state serves simultaneously as a defense against pain, and also as the storage point of it, similar to an encapsulated cyst. Body-focused psychotherapy finds and engages the trance state used to buffer pain out of consciousness, with the purpose of making it conscious and therefore accessible to the patient. True mental health has more to do with easy access to inner resources (thoughts, feelings, memories, creativity, etc.) than it does with capable coping and adaptation skills. Therapy has more to do with awakening from an unconscious trance than it does with conscious learning of new behavior.

A focus on the body in psychotherapy helps to locate the experience of feelings, and the bodily sensations associated with them. Feelings located "in the head" generally are just thought-versions of emotions, and as such, cannot translate into change. That would be like saying that owning a map of Chicago automatically gets you to Chicago. The body speaks the language of feelings in its own kinesthetic way, and simply articulating with words may not be enough to access portals of new life. We are after all, embodied creatures. We are here to embody our humanity, and that means in-the-body. For many clients, even those who have been in talk-therapy for years, the body-connection finalizes the route to full integration. "Now I get it," they say, because the body gets it.

The body as transducer, or conduit of experience, stands as the true and only arena for therapy. Thoughts and feelings as the building blocks of our experience are also physical realities located in physical places within us.   Our conscious mind emerges as only one expression of a feeling-centered molecular memory network embedded throughout the body. Psyche and Soma stand as reflective images of each other. The body contains our Unconscious. With the right type of reflective awareness, linking bodily sensation with thoughts and emotions, a full integration of fragmented past experiences can be accomplished. Our personal history then makes sense, and destiny opens up to welcome us.

"The wound is the place where the Light enters you."

~Rumi

"Your health is bound to be affected if, day after day, you say the opposite of what you feel, if you grovel before what you dislike and rejoice at what brings you nothing but misfortune. Our nervous system isn't just a function, it's part of our physical body, and our soul exists in space and is inside us, like the teeth in our mouth.
It can't be forever violated with impunity."
~Boris Pasternak
Doctor Shivago
***

"There is no state of mind that isn't mimicked in the immune system."
~Dr. Candace Pert, Ph.D
***

"When the mind is troubled, the body cries out."
~Godfather III

***

"I can't express anger. That is one of the problems I have. I grow a tumor instead."
~Woody Allen
Manhattan

2

Feelings and the Mind/Body Interface

The Invisible Factors of Healing:
The Body Follows What Is In the Heart and Mind

After years of counseling people who have received upsetting medical diagnoses, and after years of working in an Intensive Care Unit setting, I'm convinced that mental, emotional, and spiritual dimensions of experience influence the course of an illness and/or recovery. I believe that the body follows what is in the heart and mind, which is not to say that our thoughts, feelings, or spiritual beliefs directly cause or cure anything, but rather that they create the banks between which the river of bodily reality flows.

Over the years I have witnessed these "invisible factors" come into play in the illness/wellness process, quite often dominating and directing it, especially in the ICU, where such subtle influences can make the difference between living and dying. Why these seemingly elusive and unmeasurable aspects of experience have such a profound effect on the body I don't know, but common sense has always told us that they do, and now that theory is gaining support from scientists.

I have itemized the spiritual, mental, and emotional factors that contribute to healing into five fundamental categories, and written a section on each. They are:
1. the will to live
2. self-esteem
3. self-expression
4. support: the love of others
5. inspiration

The Will to Live

The will to live refers to a mysterious, imperceptible, unmeasurable experience, the absence of which can set the stage for a seemingly untimely and rapid physical deterioration and death. When the waters of hope spill out from the toppled vessel that is the body, the roots of life in the body dry up and wither. Microscopic pathogens, like vultures circling a dying beast, must somehow recognize the waning life force when the will to live flickers out, and move in to clean up. A man without the will to live is more than depressed; he is already dead. Let me recount a story.

Have a Heart

Charles' voice rang exceptionally chipper for someone being admitted to the Intensive Care Unit after a heart attack. He protested as his wife helped him unbutton his shirt, but willingly let me attach the monitor pads to his chest.

"I'm fine, really. They tell me I have a weak heart, but I feel fine." And in fact Charles was symptom-free. Except for an occasional irregular heartbeat that flickered on the screen above his bed, he looked fine. "What is this cardiomyopathy-thing anyway?" he asked with a mixture of curiosity and mild defiance.

"It seems that your silent heart attack has done more damage to the wall of your left ventricle than the doctor had thought."

"Yeah, that silent heart attack thing bugs me, too. How can you have a frickin' silent heart attack? I tell you I feel fine."

"Your doctor wants you here for observation. It might be nothing."

"Yeah, nothing."

But I could tell Charles wasn't really feeling as cocky as he lead me to believe. His left ventricle was so weakened that his cardiac output, that is, the volume of blood pumped by a single contraction of the heart, was very low. I knew this because we had hooked Charles up to a special catheter threaded through a central vein above his collar bone all the way through the valves of his heart in order to pick up temperature and pressure readings in the innermost chamber.

We could use the hydraulic properties of a closed circulatory system, along with simple core blood temperature readings, to determine pulmonary capillary pressure, which would tell us that Charles' heart had lost much of its oxygen-distributing efficiency. We could predict a downhill course for him just on the numbers gathered over a few hours--all before any symptoms of heart failure had occurred. So even though Charles insisted he still felt fine, he could tell we weren't resonating with his cocky mood. And with each new IV cardiac "med" we hooked up to the growing array of tubing and wiring at his bedside, the more worried he appeared.

Charles' second heart attack later that evening wasn't so silent. In fact it hurt. "God, it's like an elephant sitting on my chest, and it just won't quit." Sweat beaded around his eyebrows and nose, and his skin noticeably paled under the fluorescent lights. "Is this it? Am I going to die?"

"Not if we can help it," I said, pushing the morphine into the central IV port.

Charles' cardiologist ordered a balloon pump, which is a piece of equipment designed to reduce the workload of the heart by creating pressure differentials between aortic and ventricular spaces which makes the pumping process require less energy. The balloon pump is invasive to say the least. The doctor threads a tiny catheter through the femoral artery in the crotch area, up the aorta, and hooks it to a jukebox-size machine that pumps gas from a tank to inflate and deflate a 5-inch balloon the circumference of the aorta in synch with Charles' heartbeat. The doctor informed Charles he needed a new heart, and could now consider himself on the transplant candidate waiting list.

"I'm only 55. I just can't believe this is happening. I don't even feel that bad anymore." When his wife was present, Charles put on his cocky airs, partly to reassure her, and partly because she was falling apart, trying to fight back tears, to no avail. He tried humor, brashness, indifference, frustration with little things, self-distraction--whatever worked to keep his and his wife's thoughts focused on anything but him. He educated himself about heart transplantation, using the resources in our Education Department, and as the days went by, he more or less accepted his plight with a calm, hopeful spirit.

"I still feel pretty damn fine, except for this thing in my leg, and the fact that I can't get out of bed." Charles declared. He had to keep his leg straight, so that the plastic guide tube for the catheter in his crotch would stay straight and open. "God, what I would give to be able to scratch my own toes!"

The weeks went by, and no offers of a donor heart came in. The daily routine in the ICU became familiar to Charles. There were two long shifts, so the same two nurses were on duty during the week, and on weekends another crew came in. Charles got to be on a first-name basis with most of the nurses on the unit, and even those not assigned to him would drop by for little chats. Although he was no longer in crisis, the overall picture remained critical. How long this drug-and machine-induced stability could last was unpredictable.

"The crazy thing is I don't feel that bad. Are you sure there's not some huge mistake here?" he repeated again. More time passed. And Charles grew weary. Somewhere along the way, his spark to continue noticeably flickered. The cardiologist called in a psychiatric consultant who put Charles on anti-depressants and Valium. His wife continued to be stoic, and Charles did his best to make sure she remained so. But in private he confided in me that he didn't think he could take it much longer.

"This is no life for me. I can't stand the not-knowing everyday. I'm here wishing someone else is having a car wreck so that I can have their heart. What's happening to me? I just don't know if this is worth it anymore." The nursing staff knew he was depressed. We could all sense a marked change in him one morning almost two months after his admission date.

"I had a dream last night," he told me when his wife stepped out after breakfast. "You might think this is funny. I dreamed I was walking down a busy Manhattan street, carrying a bunch of colored party balloons. People were looking at me and laughing at the hard time I was having with the balloons in the wind. Suddenly I'm swept up off the ground holding on to these balloons for dear life. The wind carries me high up into the air, over all sorts of places like Central Park, and a church, and then a field of giraffes! Their necks are so long they're able to look me right in the face! I get real scared of them, but I'm more scared of letting go of the balloons, so I panic. That's when I woke up, still feeling the panic."

"Balloons, eh?" I remark, and he snorts in recognition of the unsubtle symbolism.

"Yeah, balloons. I'm afraid to hold on and afraid to let go. I can't take this any more. This is no life. I can't keep my family hanging on like this any more either."

"So what's your plan?" I asked.

"I don't know. I just can't do this any more".

"You know, Charles, a donor could show up any time now..."

"Yeah, I know, you've all been saying that."

That evening I could tell Charles had had a serious talk with his wife, because she no longer pretended to be fine. She wept openly in deep sobs as she floated in a daze between Charles' bedside and the family waiting room, where she had virtually camped out for months.

"He's given up," she told me, in shock. "He's said goodbye to me, and that he doesn't want to fight this any more. What can I do? He's asked me to let him go. How can I let him go?"

"What did you tell him?"

"I said I understood, but I really don't. How can he want to die?" The heaviness around her heart was evident in her voice.

Charles died that night, after a massive third heart attack, and with no warning whatsoever. I'm convinced that when he let go of his will to live, his body just followed suit. His mental suffering far outweighed his physical discomfort. He gave up his will to live because of it.

Self-esteem

Self-esteem is like the keel of a boat. When it runs deep and true, a person can weather great storms and upheavals. Without it, a person flounders even in the shallow waters of small challenges. Self-esteem resides at the core as a learned sense of self-appreciation, worth, and love. Like the rest of the personality, the foundation of self-esteem is set in the first few years of life. Most issues in therapy and the progress that follows, correlate with the degree of growing self-esteem in the patient.

Self-esteem can be measured by by the patient's own account and can be detected by observation. Behavior which is too loud or too quiet inevitably comes from an error in self-image or self-esteem. Bad relationships often reflect errors in self-esteem.

Self-expression and Communication Style

Self-expression and the style of communication within a family represent two invisible factors that strongly influence wellness. Honesty resides at the heart of healthy self-expression and every good communication system. "The truth shall set you free" is a stronger statement than most people realize, because speaking the truth unburdens the heart. Even criminals testify to a great sense of relief and peace after confessing their crimes. Secrets and private thoughts and feelings create isolation that breeds ill-health. Some families of patients in the ICU where I worked would purposely avoid any conversation about the reality of their feelings or the seriousness of the condition of their loved one, either to protect themselves or the patient. Often the patient in such a family system is reluctant to show anything other than cheeriness or stoicism in an effort to protect the family from pain. But in private, after the family left, those same patients would confide to me how lonely and isolated they felt, and how they wished they could share their fears and tears with loved ones. A blocked communication system relies on the forces of repression, which take their toll on the body. Conversely, I have seen families weep together openly, praise and honor each other freely, say final good-byes to each other unabashedly, and I can testify to the golden glow left in the wake of such a communication system. Whether the patient survives or not, the elements of healing are evident in the sense of peace that remains. Good communication has heart in it and that's what makes it work.

Support: the Love of Others

Closely tied to the type of communication system a person shares with family and friends is the level of support received during an illness. Group support is the equivalent of water for fish: when it's there, they thrive; without it, they gasp for life. A person without support is truly like a fish out of water, because support is part of our natural social environment. Support can be both spoken and unspoken. Group (primarily family) support feeds the emerging self-esteem of a child, sets the stage for free self-expression and good communication, and I believe is the original wellspring that nourishes our fundamental will to live. In the 1920s, a nationwide study of orphanages found that babies who were adequately fed and clothed, and yet were not held or connected with personally, mysteriously withered away and died.

One System

"One Blood, Mon," the Rastafarians of Jamaica say, an expression that signifies the unifying relatedness of us all. "One System, Mon" is what I say about the age-old body/mind debate. Body and mind are not separate systems, but rather two aspects of a single system, united by an ongoing seamless exchange between the level of biological electrochemical events and the level of personal experience. The bridge is a network of neuropeptide "mood altering" messenger molecules tagged with emotional charge. Feelings are not disembodied exieriences of some separate "mind", but rather, are contained in a very physical biochemistry that modulates and marks every bodily event within the human framework. If the body is in fact a machine, it's one that runs by feeling. Neurobiologist Dr. Candace Pert says, "There is no state of mind that is not mimicked by the immune system."

Although the term *psychosomatic* has been around since the 1920s, allopathic medicine has more recently taken large strides forward in acknowledging the connection between the "invisible" factors of heart and mind and the solely physical events of the body. Dr. Pert and her colleagues coined the term "psychosomatic network" to describe how it is no longer just the isolated physical event that can be thought of as having an emotional component, but rather the mind/body system must now be thought of as operating in an on-going feeling-driven state of being.

It was established decades ago that certain personality traits go hand in hand with specific body-system maladies. Type "A" characteristics of aggressiveness and working too hard link to the circulatory system and the heart. Type "C" personalities who don't express emotions, who deny anger, who have difficulty standing up for themselves, and who also nurture others at their own expense, seem to have a propensity toward cancer. The idea that certain emotional states, patterns of thought, and life strategies set the stage for disease in the body has recently gotten unexpected support from some pioneering insurance companies that are funding healthy lifestyle programs as a way of improving health and preventing disease.

If certain personality traits are linked with disease, are there any inner qualities of character that might bolster immune competence? Can we go so far as to tag some personality traits as bad and good?

Studies on this subject offer mixed results. First scientists claimed it was better to express anger, because keeping it bottled up can lead to inner pressure manifesting in circulatory problems and strokes. Then opinions changed when more studies confirmed that people who gave free vent to their anger tended to show more cardiac and circulatory complications. In another area of psychology, initial evidence credited nurturing parenting as creating better adjusted children, and later studies implied that parental influence has little to do with the child's development.   In yet another area of psychosocial inquiry, some researchers are firmly convinced that congeniality and service to others contribute to health, whereas others point out the cancer-prone personality profile , as documented by Lydia Temoshok and Henry Dreher, in their book *The Type C Connection: the Behavioral Links to Cancer and Your Health*, leads to a "niceness" that is a detriment to health. All this suggests that a dichotomy exists among experts in this field. So what's what? Are some feelings good and some bad?

Here's my take on this issue. We may all have the capacity to experience the same feelings, but how our inner personality traits stack up inside us is what makes us unique. How we subjectively deal with thoughts and emotions, and how we reveal what we are thinking and feeling to others, determines which feeling states are good and which are bad for us. What we express and what we repress, and under what circumstances, determines what is healthy or unhealthy, all according to the dictates of our individual biology. Expressing anger, for example, is a positive action only when doing so has a life-affirming effect. And it's not good when it doesn't.

There are no formulas when it comes to feelings, except this one: judge a feeling you're having by the way your body responds. Fuming at a boss may adversely jack up one person's blood pressure, but kickstart a healthy immune response in another. Declaring some feelings universally positive and some negative misses the subjective nature of feeling, and can itself become a stumbling block in therapy.

Feelings vs. Emotion

Feeling is the state of connected emotion, thought, and body-response. Notice that emotion is only one part of the feeling state, and that the key word in this definition is connected. Feeling is natural and universal. Everyone has the potential to feel, but not everyone does.

Have you ever known someone who's very emotional, who can cry easily over a TV commercial or during a movie, but doesn't really know what he's crying about in his own life? Or someone who can easily artic- ulate and intellectualize her beliefs and philosophies, but does so with a seeming lack of emotion or personal meaning? Or what about the person whose physical state of anxiety, tension, nervousness or sensitivity seems to dominate and rule his emotional and intellectual life? These are exam- ples of what I mean by the term disconnected state. It's essentially a state of non-feeling. Feeling has a physical, emotional, and mental component to it. When one aspect is missing, a state of non-feeling sets in. When we're not fully feeling, we engage in quests for fulfillment. When we do feel deeply and honestly, we are fulfilled. Let's examine the biology behind this, which takes us to the most sophisticated organ of our nervous system--the brain.

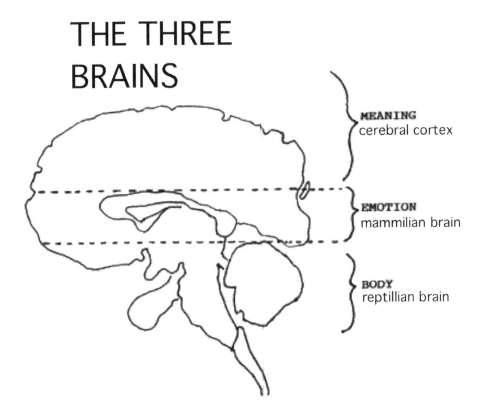

THE THREE BRAINS

MEANING
cerebral cortex

EMOTION
mammilian brain

BODY
reptillian brain

Besides having two distinct vertically-divided hemispheres, (right-brain, left-brain, with cross-wire connections located at the center called the corpus callosum), the brain also is partitioned into three horizontally divided segments, evolved over eons of time. The low-brain (often referred to as the reptilian brain: including the pons, brain stem, and cerebellum) deals with "unconscious" body functions such as breathing, blood pressure, and heart rate. It carries with it the most primitive of defense mechanisms, including fight, flight, freeze, and hide. The upper-brain, also called the neocortex or cerebrum, has to do with functions of thought and rationality, and is the section that projects meaning onto our experiences. The mid-brain (known as the "mammilian brain") contains the limbic system, a sophisticated electronic network that provides emotional charge to our experience; in other words, it processes our emotional response to the world. (The limbic system contains within it the hypothalamus, which controls the secretions of the pituitary gland, therefore making it director of hormonal equilibrium. It biologically links emotions and hormones!)

Every experience we have in any given moment (right this second as you are reading this, for instance!) has attached to it a physical response, an emotional response, and a mental comprehension of the meaning of it, all coming from the three separate parts of the brain.
The Biology of Memory

Psychoneuroimmunologists have discovered the physical basis of what we call "memory." Every biological process in the body, including thoughts and emotions, contains electrochemical components which physically encode themselves into molecules called neuropeptides. Every experience generates a neuropeptide that receives information from each of the three sections of the brain. A whole-brain response keeps these information bits united. The individual neuropeptides are then sent to specific receptor sites in the body for future reference. Memory, then, does not reside just in the brain. (If it did, our heads would swell with experience!) Memory lives throughout the body. In fact, our cells contain a perfect memory of all experiences and store it. How well we access these memories is another story. Every community has a library, but not every citizen knows how to use it. Where do these receptor sites abide? In the soft tissues of the body, including the immune system! These information-carrying neuropeptides are the mind/body link , acting as transducers of semantic and emotional information at the cellular level. Our emotions play a role in every biochemical event that transpires within us, even while we sleep.

Memory and Survival: How Feelings Move or Get Stuck

Feelings move within and throughout the mind/body system as biolgically-encoded bits of information, modulating all biological processes within us. They are designed to give us feedback about our environment at the same raw level of direct perception as our senses, and to yield insight into the motives of individuals around us. Feelings provide a cutting-edge in the mammilian game of survival by helping us be in touch.

Some feelings, by their subtlety, just like the beating heart and breathing lungs within us, live outside the realm of day-to-day consciousness. Only babies and sensitive adults feel "vibes". Other feelings, not by design, but out of a perceived sense of danger or survival, are relegated into unconsciousness. Both these subtle and the repressed feeling responses do not just go away. They circulate in the system and effect the inner landscape of mood, often warping our perceptions of ongoing reality. Feelings that were engineered to help, when rendered unconscious, hinder.

Three Communication Systems Carry Feelings

The body uses three main communication systems to handle the unrelenting traffic of prodigious amounts of moment to moment, day to day biological "information," and feelings imbibe, unify, mediate, and add a personal charge to it all. 1. The nervous system with its neurotransmitters is a rapidly moving system (think of the speed of electricity!) that involves our senses, nerves, brain, and musculature. Our emotional life mimics the qualities of nerve activity, making it subject to the laws of nerve conduction, which include flooding (overload), and gating (repression). Feelings are the barometer of our nervous system. Depression, for instance, can be viewed as impaired neurological electrical flow, and is medically treated as such. 2. The endocrine system with its hormonal messengers is a slower, cyclical, rhythmic system, subject to breakdown at many precursor phases, because one hormone relies on the secretion of another, which in turn depends on a different one, creating a chain of information transfer. As a communication system it links itself to emotions by the nature of its shared limbic circuitry, interweaving hypothamic stimulation of hormone production and emotional processing. Hormones mysteriously transfer and unlock emotional responses. Further baffling links of hormones and emotions are yet to be unraveled. Endocrinologists were surprised to discover insulin and insulin receptor sites, until now believed to be strictly involved in a pancreatic glucose-regulating function, in the brain. What's insulin doing in the brain? Could there be some overlap or shared emotional duty between hormones and neurotransmitters? 3. The neuropeptide system is older than the other two (pre-dating vertebrates in evolution), yet was discovered more recently. This system interfaces the electrical-chemical mode of the nervous system, and the widespread molecular-messenger style of the endocrine system. It is involved with chemical-electrical imprinting on large molecules called neuropeptides, so that information pertaining to the meaning, the emotional charge, and the body-response to an event is encoded and stored in a molecular library, to become part of a vast network of "understanding." Its content is comprised of all our myriad experiences, and its structure designed by the internal logic of the system. Information is stacked up deductively, rather than logically. This means that conclusions about reality and self established in childhood remain biologically dominant when new incoming information is processed, unless the processing circuitry itself is updated. This is to say that changing one's mind, especially at the belief level, doesn't come easily. Any new circuitry of perceptions and understandings is forged out of challenge, frustration, and necessity. The mind/body system, in its innate laziness, will try to force whatever has worked in the past to continue until it just can't, and even then, might continue to make futile attempts to get the desired outcome by the familiar means that never worked in the past. Think of all the futile struggles for love in abusive relationships. Rational evidence suggests that it will not happen, but the struggle continues like a phonograph needle stuck in a groove.

Memory and Imprinting

Because atoms are constantly in flux, and, according to Dr. Deepok Chopra, are shared by every cell and being in existence, past and present, our bodies are constantly being recreated. This morning's tumor owes its continuity into this afternoon to the biology of memory, and specifically to the "unwanted" memory of repressed pain. Repressed pain taxes the entire system because it requires a stress response in order to maintain unconsciousness. Blocked memories keep unhealthy conditions pocketed in our biology.

It is at the level of the neuropeptide system where "imprints of memory" set the stage for disease. Each complete neuropeptide is composed of information from each of the triune aspects of the brain---cortex, mid-brain, and low-brain--containing meaning, emotional charge, and body response. When one is overwhelmed, overload-ed, or in pain, either emotional or physical, the imprinting process gets interrupted and the neuropeptide of that event splits into fragments, or "chips." In the mind/body system's defense against pain, splitting occurs, setting into motion the centropic impulse to allow these information "bits" to reunite. Because the external "world" is no more than a canvas upon which the artistic mind/body system imprints its reality from the palette of past experience, all non-integrated past traumatic experiences in the form of encoded, disconnected bits of infor-mation inevitably intrude into the world-creating process, infiltrating the present experience of the person. This helps to explain recurring patterns in peoples' lives, and the sense of deja vu we sometimes experience. The body has been there before! The past is present until the body is updated.

Splitting for Survival's Sake

The brain's unique capacity to split experience into fragments, both along the vertical axis of the brain (which divides the right and left hemispheres), and along the horizontal axes between the triune seg-ments of lower (reptilian brain), mid-brain (mammilian brain), and the high brain (cerebral cortex), is evidence of the importance emotions have played in human evolution, especially when it comes to survival. Experiencing emotions that heightened electrical activity in the brain, which increased alertness in our primeval ancestors, and thus improved their chances for survival, wasn't enough. It also became necessary to form the ability to split off from an experience. A caveman walking across an open plain and encountering a saber-tooth tiger couldn't afford to have his fear response paralyze the system even for a nanosecond, or he'd be lunch. Thus a new and primitive defense was cultivated: the ability to split off, to dissociate from feeling. This enabled him to run like hell.

Psychological Defenses and Survival

The psychological defenses humans cultivated have stood them in good stead, because, to a certain extent, they work. They totally align with the body's prime directive of survival, and thus carry with them a potent biologi-cal imperative. In that way defenses are healthy. In concordance with Freud's brilliant hypothesis about psychic defense mechanisms such as projection, introjection, and reaction formation that stem from deeper biological brain structures, much of popular psychology holds defense mechanisms at the heart of ego function, and therefore at the root of mental health. I disagree.

Although defenses help to maintain survival, they also carry with them an innately disintegrative function for the self. By splitting off from our own experience in order to avoid perceived life-threatening pain, our psyche disintegrates, or our inner world becomes fragmented. Yesterday's defense mechanisms are now today's psychological problems. Defense-driven personalities, considered paragons of mental health in today's culture, are what Primal Therapy's Arthur Janov referred to as unreal systems. Although the defense mechanisms we created to offset pain, and the internal splitting that accompanied them, got us through childhood, and may even get us through current difficulties, they cost us dearly in the long run.

True Mental Health

Non-repressed experiences encoded on neuropeptide molecules rest on receptor sites (like little hammocks, I imagine), and create a vast inner library of memory. True mental health equates with the easy accessibility of this library, as well as a natural flexibility existing within this inner world.

Receptor Sites, Repression, and Disease

Neuro-biologists are also discovering that neuropeptide receptor sites that are vacant due to repression or internal splitting, pose a potential health hazard. Candace Pert wrote about receptor sites and the HIV virus:

"The AIDS virus, for example, enters the immune system through a receptor site normally used by a neuropeptide. Whether or not it can enter the cell depends on how much of this natural peptide is around, which according to psychoneuroimmunology theory, would be a function of the emotional expression the organism is in."

The Role of Therapy

When it comes to therapy, "biology is destiny". Treatment that ignores the central biological role of feelings cannot bring about lasting change. Mere intellectualizing doesn't cut it when it comes to imprinted, repressed pain.

Body Boundaries

The human body structurally demonstrates the fundamental and natural necessity for boundary-setting as a means of sustaining health, especially in two locales: the skin and the immune system. The skin as both our outermost organ and the site of physical contact with the world, marks where the self ends and the "outer" world begins. Also known as the "integument," it functions as the built-in delineator of our separateness and our integrity as individuals. When someone touches us lovingly and appropriately, we feel soothed, stimulated, "in touch", and connected. Gentle touch not only elicits a cascade of mood-altering endorphins and the relaxation response to make us feel good, it also triggers the skin to release thymopoeitan, a hormone which bolsters our immune competence by stimulating maturing immune cells. When someone touches us without our permission we feel "invaded" and "violated," and our fight-or-flight response kicks in, along with a gush of stress hormones, aborted digestion, elevated blood pressure, and increased muscle tension. Negative contact with the world is an emergency.

Even more dramatically, when we are without our skin--an example would be severe burn victims -- we inevitably fall prey to invasion by myriad bacteria, fungi, viruses, and other microscopic vultures in the world. We need our skin intact and respected.

The immune system, a sophisticated inner communication network designed to distinguish between inner and outer, between that which is me and that which isn't, serves as our second line of defense. When the skin has been penetrated by an outside particle, an army of Killer-T immune cells, mobilized through innate cellular intelligence and memory which deem that particle an invader, swiftly moves in to neutralize and/or kill it. Scientists didn't name them "negotiator cells" or "peacemaker cells", but rather killer cells, in full recognition that healthy boundary maintenance is built on natural destructive forces. Making boundaries is not "nice". The immune system is not "nice". It needs to be capable of demolishing outside forces. Without that capacity, the body falls prey to all sorts of microscpic predators, as seen clearly in the immunosuppressedcondition of AIDS patients. No boundaries, no survival.

Although we can easily acknowledge the benefit of aggressive immune cells within us, hostility that is used to maintain inter-personal (between people) integrity, however, is rarely welcomed or even recognized as a life-affirming phenomenon. As a result, anger and hate, as boundary-setting emotions, are commonly repressed.   When any natural flow of neuropeptide information gets blocked, including experiences tagged with so-called "negative" emotions, the body suffers. Emotional repression often shows up in the form of weak or absent boundaries in interpersonal interactions, something more readily recognized as low self-esteem.

Feelings gauge our interpersonal place in this world, and tell us whether we stand united or isolated. They act as a feedback mechanism that helps to balance our integrity as both a separate individual and as a part of greater social units. This dual nature complicates emotional responses, inevitably triggering inner conflict in the form of boundary disputes. Sometimes our emotions don't jive with the feedback from others in our environment who say we are being "selfish" when we are taking care of ourselves; they say we are being "self-centered" when we are choosing our own path rather than theirs. To whom am I loyal, and what are my priorities? Do I take care of others first? Myself first? Family first? Do I obey the norms and demands of my family or society first, or do I follow the dictates of my own heart, my own beliefs, and my own conscience?

Everyone needs a healthy sense of boundaries that balance body biology with the greater ecology of family and group systems. When these two are at odds and cannot be reconciled, and body needs are repressed in the face of cultural norms or family pressure, the stage is set for disease.

The Emotional Spectrum

What is the role of emotions in wellness and disease? Don't they interfere with clarity? Wouldn't we be better off without them? To answer these questions, we need to return to the subject of brain anatomy. An emotional response of any kind actually increases the electrical activity in the brain, the mid-brain to be exact. In terms of evolution, according to one school of thought, emotions attached to the Tree of Life and took root because of their alertness-enhancing capacity (more electricity= heightened alertness). The more awake and in-touch individuals simply tended to survive better in a hostile environment. Emotions demonstrate a "gut" level response to the environment, one that is quicker at ascertaining what is happening than the more logical "figuring out" method, the emotional approach obviously offering an edge in the survival game. Empathy also arises out of feeling, and brings with it an innate connectedness conducive to group survival.

Even the corporate world, that bastion of social Darwinism, is coming around to the emotional approach to problems, and is infusing intuitive, creative, and humanistic methods into management--all corollaries of the emotions. Emotions can also be equated with connectedness, with team, with tribe; in otherwords, with the cohesiveness of humans interacting together, either in pairs or in families. Emotions help to create bonding, attachment, and commitment, all necessary ingredients for a family or a society that wants to remain coherent and cohesive. Loyalty and patriotism are off-shoots of emotionalism.

Emotions in their most basic function have to do with an attraction-repulsion continuum, one that is commonly also divided into the "positive" and "negative" categories. Positive emotions have to do with attraction, a pulling together, a uniting. Negative emotions have to do with a repulsion, a pushing away, a withdrawing, a separating. Humans in most cultures tend to favor positive emotions because they foster human survival, and they tend to repress the negative ones because they threaten it. Even though this cultural bias against negative emotions is universal, it still behooves each individual to make peace with the "dark side" of her emotional spectrum. Without the ability to mobilize the negative emotions, the body is at risk.

Our Emotional Environment

Childhood reflects an intense boundary-sensitive period of rapidly changing perceptions of self. Initially, an infant is considered an extension of the mother and family rather than an autonomous being, and is related to as an object. Hence: "my baby", "change the baby", "hand me the baby", "the baby has my nose".

During the toddler years, a remarkable sense of self emerges. "Me do it!" is a typical first exclamation of the self as subject rather than object. As the child enters adolescence and young adulthood, she forges her own sense of distinctiveness, and establishes boundaries and intimacy with others, while at the same time creating an emotional map marked with all sorts of attraction/repulsion, intimacy-seeking/independence-asserting landmarks.

All of these experiences with their corresponding meanings are meticulously recorded, remembered, and imprinted in the circuitry of the mind/body system and unconsciously replayed whenever we interact with others and how we feel when alone. Adults who project unmet needs of childhood onto others, continue to live within the boundary framework of an infant, forever searching for a relationship that will keep an infant's world alive. Another type of adult wrestles with Mother and Father in every contact they have with others. And there are those who become stuck in the attitude of adolescence where rebelliousness, feelings of abandonment, and non-commitment reign. An adult body does not an adult make.

We find ourselves in a complex emotional environment these days, not unlike a wildly patterned quilt stitched with patches of the projected past, all inter-mingling into undecipherable personal dramas in the present. We can perceive this emotional backdrop to our current reality as varied and rich, or extremely confusing. Because of the inner baggage we each carry forward into our present world, relationships often show up like thick jungle overgrowth, and require a great deal of attention.

The path to emotional clarity involves knowing one's own healthy sense of boundaries, and learning healthy boundary-making and assertiveness skills. In the end, each of us stands alone, responsible for filling our own emotional cup, and learning how to give to and receive from others without either of those being at our own expense. Only when we integrate our own pains from the past can we fully engage in healthy, feeling relationships in the present.

Psychoneuroimmunology:
Principles of Mind/Body Integration

OK, let's recap. Biologically, we have a two-way information exchange setup that not only connects the primary internal communication systems (nervous system/brain, endocrine system, and immune system), but also links the biochemical to the experiential--all via a universal network of mood-altering molecules. Our emotional and social environment, with all its spoken and unspoken conflicts and pressures, establishes the context within which our individual organism responds. Thirteen principles govern how the translation between these levels takes place, and set the parameters for effective therapy. Here they are in a nutshell and in my own simple terms:

Principle One:
What's out there goes in, and what's in there comes out.

From the beginning, and all during the formative years of life, the nervous system is open to suggestions. It receives impressions from the environment like a passive tuning fork that vibrates from the myriad of sounds that waft by. External events thus "dominate" the nervous system, forging neural pathways which then influence all future processing. On-going exposure to a particular language, for example, imparts very specific tongue, lip, and air flow abilities, which eventually determines not just speech patterns, but how thoughts are formed, linked, and expressed. Without any conscious thought required, a map of world- and self-defining parameters is established.

Babies and toddlers naturally absorb and imitate the mannerisms of adults and siblings, manifesting those behaviors that are re-enforced by example and reward, and inhibiting behaviors deemed unacceptable by the family system. For little children facing unrealistic demands, too much resonance with external stimuli can do the reverse of what is expected, and cause inner repression.

The second part of this principle explains how our beliefs tend to find evidence for back-up. After certain patterns of perception and interpretation are imprinted in our systems, we tend to discover those things in our environment. Someone from an abusive father who concludes that "men are insensitive" will tend to filter all further contact with men through that screen.

Principle Two:
The system responds to stress long after the source of stress is removed.

An experiment that exposed puppies to continuous electric shocks to measure their immune response in the face of on-going stress, showed the immune systems dampened long after the juice was turned off. Contact with external stressors requires recovery time even after involvement ceases. The more traumatic the contact, the more recovery time necessary.

Principle Three:
The system responds to perceived/imagined reality in the same way as it does to actual reality, and to beliefs as it does to truth.

Just the memory or reminder of a former trauma can elicit a response that is identical to the original trauma. With dreams and daydreams, our mind/body system responds to inner virtual reality exactly the same way it responds to actual external reality.

Groups coached to practice basketball only in their imagination improved as much as those who practiced in actuality, and both did better than the group that didn't practice at all.

Principle Four:
The system processes input via the laws of parsimony, or the path of least resistance, which makes the known dominate new input.

This tendency to make things "familiar," or to attempt to understand a new event based on what we already know, may bring efficiency to the system, but it also yields a built-in laziness factor, and potentially robs it of novelty. The known, or familiar, comprises what we could call the "mind": an internal map or version of the world, which may or may not have anything to do with actual reality.

Principle Five:
The system maintains a record of all experiences with a   triune memory, which includes body-response, emotional charge, and personal meaning.

This holds many implications for therapy, basically requiring that the therapist deal with each of the triune factors to facilitate an integration.

Principle Six:
It takes effort to move from a trance state (where imprints from the past dominate experience and we cling to the familiar) to something new.

It requires energy to counteract the natural parsimony of the system. The familiar sits like a veil over the brand-newness of creation. The tendency to make the world familiar is hardwired in. Unconscious automation, or the old learned "knee-jerk" responses, rule unless some effort is made to dethrone them.

Principle Seven:
The system operates on the biological imperative to avoid pain.

Avoidance of pain has more survival value, and therefore more intrinsic influence on us than Freud's Pleasure Principle. Avoidance of pain is also hard-wired into the system via a complex of neurological defense mechanisms that cause the conscious mind to dissociate from trauma and fragment feeling.

Principle Eight:
Experiences repressed out of consciousness remain imprinted in the system in their original form.

Like a cyst, or anything else the body encapsulates to deal with, certain painful experiences get tucked away into unconsciousness so we can continue functioning. Unfortunately, a built-in danger follows in the wake of this principle: the body initiates an immune response to destroy any internalized foreign matter, and may perceive the vague presence of encapsulated feelings as such. Unconsciousness is dangerous. I believe this sort of dynamic underlies the auto-immune response.

Principle Nine:
The system operates on internal deductive logic.

This is not rational logic, but rather, a more "artistic" logic based on a loose set of associations and emotional charge. Conclusions about reality are based more on things verified by our feelings than anything else.

Principle Ten:
It takes energy to keep material repressed from consciousness.

That's right. Repression requires on-going vigilance to keep itself going. Defenses required to keep pain out of consciousness must be in force for the repression to be effective. When we relax or sleep, our defenses also rest. Hence the inability of repressed people to ever fully let go. Anxiety is the hallmark of slipping defenses.

Principle Eleven:
When repressed material returns to consciousness, the pain associated with it, and the energy required for the repression, does also.

This necessitates educating the client (or oneself) to make peace with pain. Learn how re-integrated pain actually forges a gateway to renewal and revitalization, so you won't resist it so much when it emerges. All the energy that went into repression gets liberated when pain is integrated. That's good news!

Principle Twelve:
Every disintegration of experience sets integrative forces into motion.

The quest for wholeness comes hard-wired in also. Things that belong whole strive to become so when split apart. In my model, the fragmented neuropeptide chips of dissociated experience begin a quest to reunite the moment they are rent asunder. The impetus to be real thus has biological fuel. This is another good news principle.

Principle Thirteen (thanks to Steve Wolinsky):
Every access is a reframe.

This makes for profoundly good news. It means that every time we consciously remember something, we change it just by accessing it. Even though the imprints of pain from age two may remain encapsulated in their original form within us, we're not two years old any more. Just by accessing the memories we alter their meaning. When we attempt reframing without full integration of feeling, however, we end up thwarting the process of fully updating our systems. Positive thinking as an overlay on top of painful feelings just becomes another neurotic strategy designed to keep us away from pain, and saps our energy from being present as much as any other neurotic thing.

Summary:

The principles of psychoneuroimmunology regulate how we process our experiences, and define "mind" as an imprinted inner mapping system that may or may not at any given moment have anything to do with as-is reality. When inner map and external circumstances fail to mesh, and inner "rules" no longer apply, a person experiences an "issue" that calls for resolution.

These psychoneuroimmunology principles also dictate what is therapeutic and what isn't, what makes for an integrative experience and what doesn't. The mind/body's healing system operates on the underlying innate movement towards wholeness, and obeys the laws of fragmentation and reintegration as mandated by the above principles.

Although many of the principles reveal our deterministic, automated, unconscious nature, just as many spotlight our capacity to enjoy consciousness, change, growth, and healing. The rudder towards freedom rests squarely in our own hands.

Let's Get Physical:
The Role of an Enzyme-Rich Diet in Emotional Integration

"...all disease must be seen in relation to feelings, for feelings predominate and integrate human functioning."
~Arthur Janov, Ph.D.
***

"Germs hover constantly about us, but they do not set in and take root unless the terrain is ripe. This terrain is cultivated by our thoughts, cognitive style, feelings, and perceptions."
~Claude Bernard, biologist

All human biological processes, from sneezing to digestion to generating red blood cells, are electro-chemical in nature. So are thoughts and feelings. The ability to access and express feelings depends on the electro-chemical health of the body. An enzyme-rich diet of fresh and raw fruits and vegetables provides the main ingredient for keeping the internal environment vital: electrolytes. Electrolytes are essentially wet minerals, the result of the body's 70% water naturally unlocking the static electrical charge of inert mineral substances from our food. Electrolytes are the building blocks of proper nerve conduction and neuromuscular functioning. Without adequate electricity at the cellular level, a person will tend to feel tired, sluggish, and even depressed. Chemical antidepressants designed to give us an emotional lift address these symptoms by keeping the gap between nerve endings flooded with neurotransmitters, thereby boosting the electrical flow. This approach misses the real source of the problem. What depletes the body of proper nerve conduction in the first place is the de-pressing of feeling, in conjunction with an electrolyte-poor diet. An enzyme and mineral-rich diet, coupled with a healthy feeling life, creates optimal health because it ensures a plentiful free-flow of electrochemical energy in the body. The life force is a physical reality you can feel.

The mind/body link-up reveals itself as a two-way mirror, where physical elements and processes are reflected in emotional and mental processes, and vice versa. The body often pantomimes the dramas of the heart and mind, and as resolution and integration find their way into the feeling aspects of our lives, so, too, does the body reflect the burgeoning health of the mind. Dealing with both aspects of the equation optimizes our chances for health.

Central to the mind/body connection is the electrical circuitry of the limbic system that dwells in the mid-brain. The limbic loop hosts the pleasure center, and is also the area central to emotion and memory. Information from this emotionally charged segment of the brain encodes itself on neuropeptide messenger molecules, which then store themselves on area-specific receptor sites throughout the soft tissues of the body.

Every physical process in the body therefore literally carries an emotional charge, as does the stored memory of each event. The mind/body system uses the level of electrical charge, or the valence of feeling, to determine what is important and what is not. Some experiences are more highly charged than others, a phenomenon that places pain and trauma (because of their high feeling valence) at the top of the biological priority list. Repressed pain thereby creates pockets of disconnected tissue that cannot receive nutrition, making them danger zones in the body, verified by MRIs and CT technology. By flushing out the physical toxins through a detoxification process that consists of eating an enzyme-rich "living foods" diet, dark spaces are brought into light--physically as well as in the consciousness of the individual.

Some levels of emotional integration are almost impossible to reach when the nutrition-depleted body cannot provide the "voltage" required for such an undertaking. Fortunately, after only a week or so of being on a regimen of fresh and raw enzyme-rich foods, inner experience shifts. Initially, you may just feel "strange." Psychological issues begin to surface, and emerging feelings signal that the body is ready for an integration. Recognize this as a good thing! A pure diet tends to make us more sensitive, and more aware of ourselves and others. Junk and heavy foods tend to buffer and blur boundary issues.

Living foods oxygenate and infuse the body with aliveness, and this initiates detoxification. Vitality equals electricity. Electricity from living foods awakens and brings to consciousness stored, emotionally charged memories that have been kept out of consciousness. Pain that has required high levels of denial and repression to cope with is released. It all comes up during detox--all the "issues" that the patient has been struggling with over time (only the pain is more direct.) It isn't easy to stuff feelings down under a regimen of raw fruits and vegetables! Pouring clean water in a dirty bucket brings dirt to the surface!

Nutrifying yourself with fresh and raw fruits, vegetables, green drinks, and wheatgrass juice, and regularly undergoing a colon cleansing, sets into motion profound transformation. Instead of the body expending energy over-taxing the large intestine, liver, and kidneys (the "eliminators") with a regular flood of junk food, it can shift into "house-cleaning" mode. The toxins that your body had to contain and isolate now circulate freely on their way to being released. Introducing a good diet after years of wrong eating flushes the dirt to the surface. Fortunately, the body's innate wisdom regulates the rate of toxic release, so that although you may experience discomfort at times, it will never be too much.

As vital as living food may be to health, it takes more than what you eat or the cleanliness of your colon to yield full aliveness. Still more fundamental is consciousness, which sets the banks of bodily reality, and determines what can and cannot be healed. Food alone can never bring full life or absolute fulfillment, nor can it ever remedy under-nourishment of heart and mind. A study of orphanages during the 1920s in the United States found that a large number of babies receiving adequate food and shelter still succumbed to an inexplicable wasting away and failure to thrive. In an atmosphere where they were not held, rocked, or attended to in stimulating, loving ways, food alone could not sustain them.

Beyond physical malnourishment, love-deprivation stands at the root of physical and mental disease. Love deprivation can mean anything from out-and-out abuse to the less extreme situation of growing up with a particular aspect of the natural self going through life unloved, unsupported, or neglected.

Negative feelings, per se, do not damage a person; but suppressing feelings does cause damage. Nature, in her unabashed simplicity, as can be seen in uninhibited children, calls for full-feeling and expression. Repression infuses an anti-life message into the body and dampens the natural state. Repression causes the body to cut off from certain parts, and waste energy by keeping feelings down. Reclaiming the heart by reconnecting with feelings clears a path through the jungle of human interactions and liberates us from the past. On-going self-discovery and self-acceptance in a practical way stands as a banner that lines the road to peace and health, whereas the "get-rid-of-it" approach ends in a tragic dead end.

The Chemistry of Tears

Once there was a man who was very emotional---that is, he wept easily, and he laughed easily. Scientists took him to a lab, and hooked him up to all sorts of measuring devices. They measured his heart rate and rhythm, temperature, blood chemistry, brain waves, etc. They got baseline values of everything, and then proceeded to show him slides, first neutral ones, and then more "emotionally charged" ones. When they showed the man slides of hungry, homeless children, he wept. And the scientists collected his tears of sorrow and spun them in their machinery, and out came a biochemical profile.

Then after more neutral slides and a return to baseline values, they showed the man another "charged" picture: a photograph of two elderly men embracing. They told him that these were two brothers separated at an early age during WWII, who were now being reunited for the first time since. The man wept tears of joy, and of course, the scientists were right there to collect those tears. These, too, they spun around in their machines and produced a biochemical read-out on them. Finally, they held up the two results for comparison, and discovered something remarkable: the chemistry of the tears of sorrow differed significantly from that of the tears of joy! Only the emotion could account for the difference! Emotions change body chemistry. Psychiatrists use the reverse of this formula: they give drugs to alter the emotions, but whichever method is used, the link abides!

Pro-active vs. Victim Mentality

People who are pro-active rather than reactive in their responses are more in control of their own destiny, more in charge of their inner response to what the world hands them, and therefore tend to be healthier all around.

Imagine an experiment actually performed on two rats, both exposed to the same mild electric shocks. One rat is trained to push a lever to prevent the current from touching either of them, while the other rat can only watch. After many rounds of being shocked, and finally learning how to manipulate the lever to protect them, a blood sample from each rat was taken to determine immune function. Conclusion: the rat that was taught to stop the shocks and ultimately did so, maintained a much higher immune function in the face of stress than did the rat who was exposed to the same shocks, but did not have the capacity to ward them off. Rat number two was a passive observer--a victim, as it were.

The following is another great example of how the pro-active state is independent of circumstances, and is conducive to health. Viktor Frankl, author of Man's Search for Meaning, and founder of the movement of existential psychology called "Logotherapy," endured years as a prisoner in four different concentration camps during WWII. Near the end of the war, conditions worsened to the point where guards were withholding food, and many inmates perished. The soldiers who finally liberated the prisoners found most of the survivors in an emaciated and sickly state. Frankl, on the other hand, looked remarkably fit. When asked how he'd done it he said, "While everyone else was being starved to death, I was fasting!"

The Past is Present

The cerebral cortex part of our brain that symbolizes and gives meaning to our experience bases its conclusions on the past. A reactive orientation is a predominantly passive mode of relating to the world, the essence of which is based in the past, meaning a person forfeits the freedom of new options when they remain attached to the hegemony of old meanings. A reactive person greets the new world with old responses. The more emotional baggage a person carries around stored in the tissue of the body, the more likely situational pressures trigger old, learned knee-jerk responses. Reactivity is largely a by-product of repressed pain.

Each one of us inhabits a space somewhere on the continuum between reactive and proactive. And everyone holds the capacity for a freedom that stands independent of circumstances, life-style, money, gender, etc. True freedom emerges from an inner experience. Freedom is fasting, when those around you consider lack of food as starving. Freedom is being able to feel in an unfeeling world.

"We are healed of a suffering only by experiencing it to the full."
~Marcel Proust

"...no man exists who was not made by the child he once was".
~Maria Montessori

***

"Our childhood is stored in our bodies."
~Alice Miller

3

Pain, Regression, Tension, and Healing

Pain: The Circuit-breaker System

The body handles overwhelming perceptions of pain or danger in rudimentary ways. In the presence of extreme physical pain, it is not uncommon for a person to pass out or lose consciousness. The primitive reptilian section of the human brain contains its own hard-wired circuit-breaker mechanism triggered by a primeval focus on survival and safety. When the electricity is excessive, the system shorts out and dis-connects. It's a simple, direct, and time-tested solution: when it hurts too much, we go to sleep.

The same response applies to emotional and mental pain--except we don't black out immediately, but rather dissociate or split off from reality, thus becoming unconscious in a more subtle way. The brain buffers us from traumatic experiences by disengaging the right and left hemispheres from each other (really!), then automatically dissects intact neuropeptide molecules into fragments, with each piece carrying a bit of the whole experience (body response, emotional response, and meaning response) away from conscious perception. When feelings splinter in this way, we can't feel it. The neuropeptide "chips," or feeling-fragments, then somehow begin to free-float in the nervous system (in the form of anxiety and/or tension), seeking to eventually reunite and find rest in a receptor site.

This psychological and physiological split, in the form of a severed memory, locks certain body-responses, emotional responses, and meaning responses into our tissues, driving us to re-create situations in our lives that reflect these feeling fragments, until they reunite in their original form within us. This theory helps to explain the biological basis for dysfunctional life patterns--why, for instance, children of alcoholics tend to grow up and find addictive partners, why we keep relating to members of the opposite sex in the same way, why we manifest food addictions. The dysfunctional behaviors are our body's unconscious attempt to integrate original painful experiences that we had to split from in order to survive.

One client of mine understood this when he exclaimed, "I've needed to feel cheated by people over and over again in my life, because I already felt cheated inside. It confirmed what I already knew to be my truth."

Cognitive psychology would have us believe that how we think determines how we feel. However, although one's frame of mind influences feelings to a degree, brain physiology and evolution show that feelings come first. Our more primitive reptilian and mammalian brains dominate, and dictate to the cerebral cortex what is subsequently processed symbolically into language, dream image, or philosophy. The "thinking" brain follows the feeling and sensory brains, acquiring raw material from them, out of which it then forges story and meaning. Biologically, emotion comes first, and thinking comes second. Emotionally-charged memory, even when unconscious, dominates the inner hierarchy of what gets our system's attention. It cannot be erased--it can either be repressed, or be made conscious, and then integrated.

Unfortunately, the body/mind system, in an attempt to free itself from pain, often treats unconscious imprinted memories as it would a splinter, or any other foreign invasion: it launches an immune reaction to get rid of it, even though the "it" is actually one's own feeling response to trauma! The "get-rid-of-it" mindset of coping with pain thus has its roots in biology. I believe autoimmune responses, when the immune system attacks healthy parts of the body, are misguided self-protection attempts. Unlike the wolf who, in desperation, chews off its own trapped leg in order to survive, an autoimmune response serves no real survival function.

Inner shut-down and dissociation occur as knee-jerk responses when memories and mindsets forged and adopted long ago in our personal history are triggered by something in the present. It happens without thought or conscious intent. The mind in the grip of past trauma is so defensive and reactive that it loses the ability to access creative adult resources and options. Without any awareness whatsoever of our repressed inner state, we live hemmed in by our own limited beliefs, lost in the struggle for what we never had, and held back from growing up altogether. Yesterday's defenses and survival reactions rob us of today's possibilities.

Neonates Feel Pain

For years, surgeons operated on premature babies without anesthesia believing that even if the infants felt the pain, they wouldn't remember it. New research with rats suggests that the body does remember the pain and is forever changed.

A study using newborn rats at the National Institutes of Health (NIH) found that painful trauma mimicking medical procedures commonly performed on preemies made the lab animals much more sensitive to pain as they aged.

The reason is that pain causes the developing nervous system of the very young to grow more nerve cells that carry the sensation of pain to the brain, NIH researchers say.

The study is part of a continuing effort by medical science to understand how and when the nervous system develops and how the growth of nerve tissue is affected by stimuli like pain. Such research has a direct bearing on efforts to save and improve the lives of infants born before the normal 40-week gestation is up. Survival of babies born up to 15 weeks prematurely is now not unusual, but it takes a major medical effort and many painful procedures, including countless needle sticks, breathing tubes, and even surgery.

Other studies have shown that premature babies tend to report more pain in their childhood years, and their parents report that these children's pain response is greater than their siblings'. (reprinted with permission from Nursing Spectrum August 21, 2000 Vol. 10, No. 17, page 27)

Four Worlds, Three Brains
Our Brain Creates a World

Every living organism with a brain creates a separate world with its brain, and then proceeds to live within the parameters of that world. Kittens raised from birth in a special environment consisting exclusively of polka dots and curved surfaces, and then placed in a room with squares and straight edges, stumbled all over themselves, fell down stairs, and bumped into walls. Their internal map no longer matched the terrain.

When this mismatch of inner map and external reality takes place in humans, they often seek help. Old ways of thinking, and old behaviors inevitably fall short in providing adequate solutions in new, unfamiliar circumstances. Some people simply "try harder" with old strategies formed in their developing years, and end up banging their heads against what shows up as more and more undoable. Those clients seek out therapy primarily to make the discomfort of difficult transitions "go away". They focus on reducing the tension inherant in encountering new things, and thereby deeper entrench themselves in the rut of old habits. When they continue to refuse or avoid the challenge of change, the therapist may actually try to intensify the Unworkable, to frustrate the old map-maker brain even more, and hopefully coax the patient to eventually birth herself into a new-world grid of possibilities. Sometimes things need to get worse before they can get better.

On the other hand, some people seek change head on. The

stress of encountering the Unworkable moves them to learn new ways to engage their problems. Struggling harder to change others or the environment as a way to make things better is no longer good enough. The shift they seek lies not necessarily in the outer world, but rather within their own internal map, or even more deeply, their map-making style.

Lazy Brain Syndrome

Unfortunately, the brain prefers familiar, old maps, even in people who actively want to change, and so the "known" is given precedence. If you follow the same route to work every day for many years you will naturally gravitate to the interior automatic pilot of familiarity. The narrowed, parsimonious focus of that type of "brain-efficient" behavior is the trance people fall into. Repetition, and thus, familiarity, invokes a trance state that requires minimal alertness. The reticular activating system (RAS) at the base of the brain somehow determines the degree of alertness required in any given situation, (unexpected situations require more alertness, familiar ones require less) then channels it to the appropriate areas of the brain, where coping mechanisms kick in. The brain prefers the path of least effort, and delegates more and more of a person's routine involvements into the lower levels of alertness. Automatic pilot is the brain's modus operendus of choice.

"Alertness" or "consciousness" beefs up electrical brain activity. So does pain. Pain boosts alertness at a time when we may need it, but then, because it hurts, don't want it. Emotions, because they increase electrical activity in the brain just as pain does, also "up" the alertness factor. Even grief, although a "down" feeling, marks high electrical activity. Grief is a feeling, the body's natural response to loss. Depression, on the other hand, is the hallmark of low electrical brain activity, not because of sad feelings, but because of the depression of feelings. Depression, because of its numbing effect, is not a feeling state, but rather is a defense against pain.

Feelings are a mixed blessing. They keep us in touch with the subtleties of human interaction and foster bonding, but also bring a heightened awareness of pain. We need to have feelings in order to be alert enough to survive danger, and yet we need to be able to repress them so we won't suffer. It is this evolutionarily hard-wired dilemma that makes change so hard.

The ever-efficient, lazy brain leans towards the familiar, thus resisting change. Because of that, the circuitry responsible for creating a new inner-world map is reserved exclusively for emergencies. Only in the face of the Unworkable, the Unknown, and the Uncomfortable does the brain scream out for a new world and move beyond its self-imposed trance-like limitations. Nothing screams louder for change than pain. When pain is repressed, the scream doesn't go away, it just gets muffled. In extreme cases, this cry will manifest as a suicidal tendency. The person experiences a deeply felt understanding that something needs to radically change in order to be free from the damned-if-I-do, damned-if-I-don't, unworkable scenario and its pain. What is obvious to the therapist, but not to the client, is that the body doesn't have to die in order to get past the pain.

Map Making

Reality map-making begins before birth. Even in the womb, the developing brain, in response to its environment via simple kinesthetic and sensory feedback loops, along with emotional input from the Mother-host, lays into its own neural circuitry a map of "how it is." The descriptive map of "how it is" soon turns into a prescriptive mapping process in the form of assumptions, predictions, and rules. Have you ever navigated a car, found yourself at a dead-end, gazed unbelievingly at your map, and said, "We can't be here!", as though the map was dominant over reality? In the same way, birth into this reality from the "wombal" world is a transition that cannot be computed by the brain circuitry set within the womb. Our subjective interpretation of our birth experience comes from the old circuitry. (This applies to all understanding: it's based on old information.) Because each new experience is the end of the old, birth easily gets construed as a death. Birth dramatically terminates an essentially tranquil world, and its accompanying body and emotional response of terror becomes imprinted and generalized to include any sense of impending change as a threat.

Transitions like birth, with all the overwhelmingly incomprehensible new input, knock the world-creating nature of the brain for a loop. Disorientation and confusion ensue. Think of the culture-shock and heightened mindfulness that occur when traveling in a foreign land. Every billboard, plant, facial expression, and smell comes at us with a sense of novelty lost to us in our home turf where we take everything for granted. Encountering newness makes us more vigilant, because we need extra awareness to help us through the initial phases of disorientation and confusion.

"Total immersion" into a new environment induces the most dramatic learning, but also the most disorientation and confusion. Although they make us uncomfortable, frustration, confusion, and the tension of not-knowing may be necessary ingredients for change, as well as vital ingredients in productive therapy. Therapy either accesses this level of brain functioning by frustrating old mind-sets, and encountering confusion, or it merely offers band-aid treatments. Sometimes good therapy feels threatening, and it is--to the part within us that clings to the status quo!

The map-making process of the human brain is governed by the ever-changing feedback exchange between organismic need and the environment. Although the basic needs for nourrishment, safety, love, and stimulation may remain constant throughout a lifespan, they, of course, vary in priority and form as we grow up. The younger and more dependant we are, the stronger the focus on pleasing and/or adapting to others. Dependent and co-dependent behaviors have their roots in thwarted development because they represent an earlier time of life.

Making a Case for Healthy Regression

I've seen clients' lips and nostrils turn blue as they gasp for oxygen on my office floor. I've heard them cry for Mommy and Daddy in a toddler's voice. I've seen forcep marks reappear on a forehead in the reliving of a birth. I've witnessed clients shake and sweat as memories of early childhood abuse errupted into their consciousness . I've heard full-grown adults wail like babies in ways they could not do on purpose. So when I write about regression in therapy, I'm not only bias, I'm an extremist. I've had to stretch my therapeutic perspective to include what might seem like a bizarre cosmology. I'm convinced that a healthy, orderly regression to the incompleted early stages of one's own development is essential for deep healing to take place.

According to myth, when Buddha was born he strode out of the womb, enlightened, and able to speak. Except for him, nobody starts off fully mature. On the road from birth to adulthood, we develop physically, emotionally, cognitively, and morally in incremental stages documented by the giants in the fields of individual, social, and cognitive psychology—Sigmund Freud, Erik Erikson, and Jean Piaget, to name a few. Transpersonal psychologist and former LSD researcher, Dr. Stan Grof, maintains that these developmental "bands of consciousness" that go all the way back to peri-natal days remain within us as the foundation of our current experience. As Swiss Psychoanalyst, Alice Miller, said, "Our childhood is stored in our bodies. Our conscious mind, like the flower of a plant, grows out of the stem of our biologically-encoded history."

The origin of our identity goes even farther back than childhood. From the time we begin life as a single cell, we individually recreate the evolution of all animals on earth, transforming morphologically from amoeba to fish to salamander to mammal to primate to human. Our brain follows that same evolution, as does our growing consciousness as individual human beings. We start off primitive, vegetative and small, unaware of anything but our immediate surroundings, cultivate the ability to emotionally and socially bond, and progress all the way up to pocess a sophisticated analytical, symbol-making neocortex, by which you are now reading and understanding this book. Unbeknownst to the conscious mind, we carry within us the collective memory of every prior stage of evolution. And every earlier stage of our own brain's development.

We all roughly grow up according to the same blueprint, and go through the same phases. These developmental changes do not take place in a vaccuum, but rather in an atmosphere of need. Without parental love, nurturing, and sensitivity at every stage, normal, let alone optimal, growth is disrupted, and a grid stays active long after it is naturally due to go dormant. When needs are not met, the views, beliefs, and feelings of childhood linger.

When feelings become fragmented in the response to pain at any early stage in life (and I'm maintaining that this is a sure bet), development is either arrested or prematurely accelerated, and a smooth transition from one grid to the next is impaired. Integration of a feeling repressed in an earlier grid of development requires regression back to that same grid when a patient enters therapy. The same map-making part of the brain involved in the split must be involved in its renewed wholeness. Repressed feelings from age 5 must be accessed and integrated from within the original mind-grid within the client. The same holds true for splits that occur even earlier, as far back as the womb. Those integrations will look very different from each other because how a five-year-old experiences pain is very different from how a fetus does. Any therapeutic intervention short of regression to the grid within which the split took place is symbolic, and leaves the disruptive effects of that repression intact.

> *"Every system strives to be conscious because consciousness means survival."*
>
> ~Arthur Janov

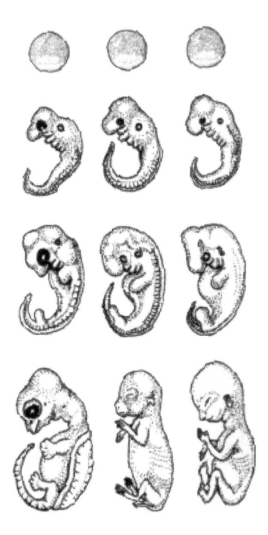

From Lizard to Mammal to Human

That's why cognitive therapy alone may help us know about our pains without necessarily changing the dysfunctional patterns that result from that pain. The adult mind can compensate for but cannot integrate childhood pains.

By the nature of their narrow scope, mind-grids are limited in their ability to handle discordant events, and so inner conflict is inevitable. As in the card game, War, inner world grids clash, to the point where the struggling person experiences anxiety and an "issue." Without integration, the issue is handled by having one world-grid dominate another.

Here's an example: one of my adult clients actually complained, "If I go to a place and I'm hot, I have to open the windows, and if I'm cold I have to put my jacket on." She whined about how she had to be responsible for her own comfort wherever she went. Imagine that! To cling to the Wombal world, with its unspoken credo of "everything is done for me with no effort on my part," as the dominant reality in her life was this woman's mission. Can you imagine a world so out of whack as to require her to be responsible for her own comfort? This particular patient was a "reformer," and an "educator," intent on designing an outer world to fit a Wombal model. (This is not meant to imply that there is no room for reform or education, but from the way this client was carrying out her mission, it was doomed from the start!) She experienced the world as a hostile place, and maintained a high level of frustration and defeatism. Eventually her antagonism manifested in her body in the form of numerous severe allergies. This is what can happen when we refuse to be in the world with rules that go beyond the womb! Even at age 40, this same woman lived via a strong financial umbilical connection to her parents. Her helpless, dependant behavior, aberrant thinking, and misplaced affect all added up to severe "mental illness". Drugs didn't help her. What did was regression back to the the earliest of visceral pains that she experienced when her wombal needs were thwarted. Her repressed pain had been fueling a whole life of insanity and misery.

Different parts of the brain coincide with the different world grids I am proposing. The Wombal World grid is associated with the primitive, reptillian brainstem, the Primal and Adolescent World Grids, with the mammilian mid-brain, and the Adult World Grid, with the neo-cortex.

Dr. Ernest Rossi, confirming this theory in his 1986 book, **The Psychobiology of Mind/Body Healing**, asserted that the limbic system, at the core of mid-brain activity, serves as the "transducer" between the semantic and mechanical. The same circuitry that is involved in processing emotions translates verbal (or semantic) information into a mechanical (or body) response, linking a body response with a verbal conclusion about reality. Feelings thus reside at the core of real therapy and real change, not just by decree of a humanistic school of psychology, but as proven by the study of human biology.

When Inner Worlds Collide: "From Tissue to Issue"

Many problems, concerns, or conflicts experienced via the neo-cortex, thinking part of the brain reflect repressed pain from lower levels. When we don't feel emotional or visceral pain directly, we channel it into a more conscious level of experience where it takes the form of an "issue." We rationally "work out" the pain we refuse to feel, don't go the full distance to integrating it, and end up dragging out and postponing that integration. The issue continues, and finds new forms. When pain is fully integrated at a feeling level, issues dissolve.

The urgency of a need disappears as the need is met. Thirst disappears when we quench it, and intensifies the longer it goes unquenched. The incompleteness and unresolvedness of a need unmet, or repressed, at any level of development, then re-shapes into a higher function mode such as philosophy, beliefs, theology, etc. You can learn a great deal about someone's level of feeling or repression based on his life philosophy. Pessimism as a mental outlook naturally emerges from a painful history of mismatched needs and fulfillments. A self-avowed racist, as another example, has corralled his personal pain into a cortical philosophy of hate and separatism. His ideas scream out loud the pain his brain is silencing.

Lets return for a moment to the definition of a trance, which was explained earlier. Whenever there is a narrowing of focus, combined with relaxing repetition, the body enters a state similar to the early stages of REM sleep, where the brain disengages from the outer senses, emits slower brain waves, and tunes in to its own internal map of reality. In a trance we are more influenced by inner already-assimilated (and hence, past) impressions than by any new external contacts. Dreams, as the interior pictures painted by the brain, completely independent of sensory involvement with the external world, are truly the "royal road to the Unconscious" as Freud said, and are also the deepest of trance states. They contain symbolic versions of feeling fragments seeking integration.

Humans seek out trance states because of the relaxation and the fact that in a trance the conscious thinking mind stops, nothing feels urgent, nothing is compelling. A trance fills the mind with familiar images and the body with soothing sensations. (Television facilitates a passive, trance-like state, which explains its popularity.)

A trance state for a baby is easily elicited by rocking, and repetitive cooing and patting. The trance state for a fetus is filled with oceanic surround-sounds of blood flow and heart-beat in a world of total free-floatation. These may very well be the trance states humans seek to emulate the most.

Trance states that have the most emotional charge are the most potent over time, that is, they linger the longest, strongly influencing future engagements and experiences. The minute the first Christmas decorations start going up, I am instantly transported into my "Christmas trance," which includes body and emotional responses that reach all the way back to my first encounter with Santa Claus. The emotional charge of an event is the body-mind's way of tagging it with a gradient of importance to survival. Trances further survival by keeping us calm. Depression is a form of trance that calms us by numbing out pain. If you don't feel it, it won't hurt. Unconsciousness, as the ultimate trance, has found a central role in human life because of its survival value. Unconsciousness helps us keep going.

As each world-grid created by the brain has an investment in numerous trance states because they maintain the status quo of a familiar map, and because change and the possibility of a new outcome often depends on the death of an old way of looking at things, the therapist has the daunting task of helping the client snap out of trance living. As a therapist, I find myself in the business of awakening. Because unconsciousness keeps us comfortable and away from pain, waking up is hard to do.

Each of the four grids exists as a segmented area of the brain's mapping abilities, as well as a sub-stratum of the individual's consciousness. How we experienced the world as babies, for instance, lives within us as a sub-grouping of our total map-making abilities, and when conditions are "right," we might revert to that baby-world as our primary mode of engagement or interaction. In face of stress, as seen especially in the case of a severe trauma like a plane crash or a rape, people regress to a more basic, primitive form of being-in-the-world, confirming that a sub-stratum of infantile circuitry secretly co-exists with more mature mind-sets, in a seemingly adult framework. Stroke patients, too, are known to revert to earlier modes of map-making and relating when the more adult features of their brain physiology are incapacitated.

I am also suggesting that fragmentation of feeling into repressed pieces of experience outside our conscious awareness exerts an on-going regressive tendency in the psyche that we often fight with our more rational, adult frames of mind. Therapy based on a natural integrative rather than on a "get-rid-of-it" model makes the space for regression to happen, recognizing it as central to the healing of old feelings. What often keeps a person "intimacy-impaired" as an adult are the hurts and conclusions of childhood. True updating, beyond mere behavioral changes, requires regressing to the original feeling state.

If you lose your wallet on the way to your destination, you must backtrack in order to retrieve it. Instead of unconsciously staying in the area where you lost your wallet and never moving on, therapy in this context is about backtracking in order to move forward. A good therapist knows the difference between healthy regression to the past and wallowing in the past.

The child within us lives as a trance-identity in many varied forms.

The level of influence old world-grids have on our current reality varies for each of us. The core essentials remain similar enough for me to generalize about what it is to be stuck within each grid. Let's start with babies.

The body itself is governed by two binary, polarized structures: we have a right brain and a left brain. We have a central nervous system with a sympathetic branch and a parasympathetic branch. Just as you can see only one side of a double-sided coin at a time, only one of these polar aspects can be dominant at a time. You can't do math and poetry at the same time. You can't do karate and digest your food at the same time. It is possible when opposites are not reconciled well in consciousness, to end up with a person at odds with an entire half of his or her own psyche, whether it has been repressed, avoided, or is still in conflict. A man can be so macho and homophobic, for instance, in order to completely disown his sensitive, feeling side. I strongly suspect autoimmune diseases pantomime this kind of inner struggle. I strongly suspect cancer is the manifestation of unsuccessfully trying to encapsulate something "unacceptable," (sexual or aggressive feelings, for example). Treatment must then involve making the unacceptable acceptable; the bad, good; the unlovable, lovable. Therapy must engage a person's ability to perceive and regard both polarities as part of the whole. Remember, even though we can only see one side of a coin at a time, we can feel both simultaneously. Feeling carries out the integrative function of the body and brings the hope of ultimate inner reconciliation. Both inner and outer reconciliation of opposite forces and a healthy tolerance of dichotomies are the victory trophies on the mantle of inner work, and naturally follow in the wake of deep feeling integration.

Tension: Bane or Boon? Backwards or Forwards?

"The neurotic seeks to reduce tension by going backwards.
The artist seeks to resolve tension by creating."
~Arthur Janov

Let's talk about tension. Physiological tension manifests as bodily tightness that accompanies a restrained, inexpressive state of being. The muscular armoring of a tense system reflects a defensive stance in life, and has anxiety coursing through it as its shadowy companion, an anxiety that free-floats in the form of loose, unsuccessfully repressed feeling-fragments. A person can be either predominantly anxious or predominantly tense. Both conditions stem from feeling fragmentation. A person riddled with repressed feelings inevitably lives in the world with struggle and tension.

Psychological tension could be called mental uptightness--a rigidity of thought, along with a limited range (if any) of emotion. Psychological tension, too, remains rooted in the mind's defense against feeling. People who look to release tension or relieve anxiety through sensory or mental distraction, sexual release, drugs, or alcohol, never completely resolve the discomfort, but merely reduce it temporarily.

Structural tension, the brainchild of Robert Fritz, composer and teacher, refers to a healthy form of tension that propels creativity. In his book, *The Path of Least Resistance*, Fritz refers to structural tension as the inherent tension in changing systems that fuels the change process. When someone wants to move from point A to point B, that desire creates a tension--a forward-propelling pressure. As long as she remains true to that vision of Point B, the accompanying tension aids her movement in that direction. Think of stretching a rubber band between two hands--the hand that lets go automatically launches the rubber band towards the other hand. Releasing the rubber band without the tautness or tension is completely ineffective. Release without tension renders the action ineffective.

Robert Fritz's model looks like this:

He rightfully advises us to "keep psychological and physiological tension out of it!" in order for the creative process to fully benefit from structural tension, and as a result, come to full fruition. His advice includes educating ourselves to easily recognize the difference between unhealthy and healthy tensions, and to ignore the unhealthy ones.

Below is my revision of Fritz's model, the premise of which maintains that the process of projecting into the future and manifesting a desired outcome must take into account the emotional level at both Point A and Point B stages, otherwise it remains one-dimensional, cerebral, and impotent.

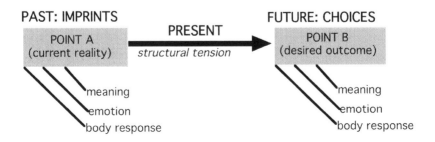

Point A and Point B each have their own energy. Point B energy carries the excitement of a fulfilled dream, and Point A energy contains a paralyzing inertia, the blocks to forward movement in the form of fear, doubts, or limiting beliefs. I firmly believe we must recognize that what we call the "current reality" of Point A has deep roots in the past. What I now have in my life is a direct result of what I believe possible and desirable. Beliefs like that stem from the past. The only way to keep psychological and physiological tension from interfering with Fritz's elegant model of manifestation is not to ignore or attempt to bypass those tensions, but rather to consciously attend to, and tap into, those elements for empowerment.

Too frequently, by mistaking structural tension for psychological and physiological tension, we attempt to reduce the discomfort produced when those tensions arise. When we seek to relieve tension, and not resolve it, we sell a potentially creative process short, and live with our cups empty, dependent on others, or upon serendipitous circumstances, to fill us. Robert Fritz calls that placid way of being the "Reactive Orientation." The results of this approach to life hardly satisfy us. We use others to remove our pain, all in order to make ourselves feel better. When people learn to "relate" in this way, they want their cup to be filled by others, to have others alleviate their loneliness, or take care of them. This kind of behavior establishes a blueprint for resentment and frustration, and yet, ironically, it is often considered normal. Working with structural tension, as opposed to attempting to reduce psychological and physiological tension, ensures that our cup is already full at the onset of our interactions with others. Passion is the fuel of structural tension.

Therapy and Structural Tension

A therapist also needs to be aware of the differences in tension, and not mistake structural tension for physiological or psychological tension. The job of the therapist is not only to help relieve the anxiety or stress involved in Point A, but also to help the client discover what he or she truly wants (Point B), which can actually increase the tension in the system. A person with a history of abusive relationships may simply give up wanting a good one, or not even believe a healthy relationship is possible, because it seems that the desire for one has been at the root of the pain. A person who has been battling a disease may no longer wish to feel hope, for fear of having it dashed again. Someone else carrying a life-long thought pattern of undeserving-ness, or less-than, may never at all have set her sights on true fulfillment! Because desire fuels creativity and manifestation, part of my job as a therapist is to help a client rekindle that flame. A system fraught with psychological and physiolgical tension still may need a healthy infusion of passion to get it moving, even though that passion makes all the tensions rise.

True fullfillment is full-feeling, where I feel my current reality with no resistance or defense. My heart is free to manifest structural tension with which to creatively propel myself forward, according to my own desires. As I release my hold on current reality by letting it be, with no resistance whatsoever, the body/mind system releases the hold the past has had on me and opens me up to receive the future.

How many people try to use the present to heal the past! Some therapies focus on providing "corrective emotional experiences" to help neutralize past traumas. This happens through both a loving, attentive therapist, or a supportive family-like group. Hear this: the present cannot heal the past. As good as having loving people in the present may be, they cannot fill the broken cup of the past. Only feeling can mend that. Although we cannot heal the past by filling the present, we can fill the present by healing the past. The past is constantly present as body tension, and will remain so until that tension is resolved. Only then can we generate a healthy structural tension within us that will enable us to proceed into our own future, open to receive what we truly want.

The Difference Between Suffering and Pain

Pain hurts. Suffering is being in a continual state of pain without the hurt. When pain is repressed it doesn't just go away. It goes in. You can leave your feelings but they don't leave you. A person carrying unfelt pain inevitably suffers.

So what hurts? When a need goes unmet, it hurts. Our needs change, of course, throughout our development. Whenever a need goes unmet, and we repress the pain of it, we stop growing. Children can't bring themselves up, either physically or psychically. We need food, shelter, and parenting. When those needs aren't met, they remain frozen in time and space, embedded in the tissue of our body and in the memory of the cells. Every reminder that occurs in the present that is vaguely reminiscent of the original precipitating painful event will elicit suffering. Pain cries out to be integrated.

We perpetually re-create unfinished inner situations from the past where pain sits at the core precisely because we're not finished with that pain. Each day we either successfully repress the pain all over again, or we succeed in feeling it and moving forward. Pain that is not allowed to be felt follows us like a shadow of suffering. How paradoxical that our method of protecting ourselves from pain (repression) actually perpetuates it. How paradoxical that the path of feeling one's pain leads to the healing of the suffering heart.

Individuation

Individuation, a word coined by C.G. Jung, the father of Depth Psychology, to describe the lifelong process of development from an undifferentiated conglomerate of cells into a unique, autonomous, separate, inter-dependent, aware individual, is strongly influenced by sexuality. Lust mobilizes the integrative forces that move us either forward or backward in consciousness. We know when we are moving backward when sleep, lethargy, sameness, and rigidity of thought and action prevail, and we know we are moving forward when we change and grow in alignment with our inner sense of excitement, fulfillment, and destiny.   Homeostasis, or the self-regulatory, stability-seeking mechanism that helps us keep an even keel from moment to moment, is flexible in this case, which leaves the rudder of this ship in the hands of free will. Forward or backward, conscious or unconscious is up to you.

Those who have learned to successfully integrate the challenges of life with awareness tend to resolve tension through creativity. They embrace change, and navigate forward. But people who engage the world resisting change, resolve tension through discharge and distraction (yes, this means sex, drugs and rock and roll) eventually discovering that their coping methods push them backwards in terms of their individual growth. The manner in which we resolve our tension reveals a lot about who we are, because we are either using our inner resources to grow and develop, or we are resisting what is new, thus maintaining the status quo. Forward motion along the path of individuation, is far more life-affirming and dynamic than a mere discharge-oriented self-maintainence.

The need to Individuate drives us relentlessly because it is a built-in possibility. It beckons us all. Unlike the involuntary expression of evolution, an adaptive process over many generations of trial and error, mutation, and selectivity, human individuation happens by choice alone. The context of a person's family and community can either enhance or inhibit the urge to individuate, but they do not create it. True heroes individuate no matter what their circumstances.

A structural tension exists within us between a sense of ourselves as a separate person, and a sense of ourselves as part of a unity constantly interacting with others. That unresolved conflict sometimes causes us to link with others sexually, for resolution and completion. Depending on our deeper life orientation, whether we on one hand choose the path of individuation, or on the other hand, as philosopher, Frederick Nietzche said, the path of "blending with the herd", we either seek out partners who help us feel better through unconsciousness or those who subconsciously match our inner yearnings to be whole. Sex is very different in these two orientations-- one based on the innate electrical imperative that comes from protoplasmic excitability, and the other based an innate archetypal imperative to grow and become.

Sex Mask

Because our emotions sometimes add an unpleasant "charge" to our life experiences, and sex offers a discharge, people often use sex to mask uncomfortable feelings. Sexual stimulation, which provides touch, excitement, a sense of safety and pleasure, is often purposefully introduced into painful feeling situations for the sake of making the pain go away by somehow overriding it. It isn't too far-fetched, either, to think it possible to balance or neutralize pain by adding pleasure. People who use this strategy in the face of emotional pain are too often disappointed, because in fact one does not cancel out the other.

Sex inevitably masks some aspects of the indivduation process. By using sex to diminish tension, without achieving some resolution or integration of pain, we veil a deeper inner reality by engaging sexually rather than holistically, and end up camouflaging avoidance. Using sexual anesthesia as a way to buffer the inevitable discomforts and confrontations of relationships keeps a person immature and intimacy-impaired.

Childhood Sexual Abuse

More than any other sexual experience, childhood sexual abuse sets in dysfunctional patterns which hugely influence one's sexuality for life, often freezing into space and time the child's confusion about pleasure ("feeling good is bad"), embodiment ("to survive I must leave my body"), gender ("bad things happen because I have breasts"). Where the body played such a central role in the early trauma, a focus on bodily-reality in the healing emerges as paramount. To think intellectual insight or understanding alone can heal sexual trauma, without accessing the body's response, is delusional.

Brian: Do It Now!

Brian, an athletic 34-year-old with years of history as a sex-a-holic, frequent visits to adult book stores, masturbating, and one-night-stands, sat in my office after months of therapy, and a hard-fought week of the sexual abstinence I had recommended.

"I am so jittery, and uncomfortable! I did what you asked--no sex for a whole week, and I can't stand it any more! I've got to get some release!" He lies down on the sofa in my office, as he's gotten accustomed to doing in the course of getting in touch with feelings and body sensations in therapy.

"I've got to have an orgasm! I really want to cum!" he shouted, writhing and squirming. "I can't stand feeling this way any more!"

"Say that again!" I urged.

"I can't stand feeling this way any more! I want this feeling out of me!"

"What feeling, Brian?"

"I feel so....bad."

"Feel it. Sink into the feeling. Let it happen this time. You've whacked this one off enough! Let it happen! Who's the boss here? You or the feeling?"

And he writhed and screamed, even as he experienced an erection and a strong desire to discharge. He wiggled, contorted, whimpered, whined, and groaned for a solid two hours, sometimes looking and sounding like an adult, sometimes like a baby. He revisited this particular deep agony many times in the office, bit by bit allowing it to be there without running from it, letting the full impact of his own experience finally catch up with him.

At a group feedback session, he shared this insight: "This is what made me sexually addicted, I know it. I've hated this awful feeling inside me, of not being wanted, of needing so much touch and being rejected. It all came together (sic). I have been using sex to make me feel better, but I could never get enough. This awful feeling just came up again and again. I've never let it come close before. Now I know what's been driving my urges. I thought I was just a super-sex freak or something. But that's not it!"

My commitment as a therapist is to help unravel the threads that strangle the free-flow of natural health, and help reweave them into a reality that is liveable, workable, and in alignment with the true destiny of the client. Lust is a many-splendored thing. When it twists into inner and outer misuse and abuse, it cries out to be healed. Every therapist, then, is a sex therapist.

"I believe the greatest gift I can receive from anyone is to be seen by them, heard by them, to be understood and touched by them. And the greatest gift I can give is to see, hear and listen, to understand and to touch another person."

~Virginia Satir

"First try to discover your own childhood, then take the experience seriously. Listen to the patient and not to any theory; with your theory you are not free to listen. Forget it. Do not analyze the patient like an object. Try to feel, and help the patient to feel instead of talking to the patient about the feelings of others."
~Alice Miller

***

"The main interest of my work is not concerned with the treatment of neuroses but with the approach to the numinous. But the fact is that the approach to the numinous is the real therapy and in as much as you attain to the numinous experiences, you are released from the curse of pathology."
~Carl Jung

***

"The power to touch a heart--never underestimate that."
~Prem Rawat

4

Inner Work: The Inner Dimension of Bodywork

If you as a bodyworker don't talk to your client, then read this section to inform yourself on what psychotherapy looks like , and not as a guide on what to do. I hope you enjoy....

Off-balance, Right-On!

One time in the Intensive Care Unit I overheard a group of doctors huddling together about a critically ill patient that they were only able to stabilize with massive drug and life-support therapy, and who was nevertheless slowly slipping downhill. It made for one of the strangest medical conversations I've ever witnessed, and has become a hallmark of my Centropic Integration™ approach to therapy.

"We've got to do something radical at this point," said the nephrologist, "or else the kidney failure alone will do him in."

"I agree. He's not breathing on his own and the longer he's on the respirator the more he'll get hooked to it. Stabilizing him is just buying us a little time and he's going fast. If we don't come up with something , he'll be dead in a couple of hours--or even worse--on these machines for days."

" Yes, stability is not in his favor at this point, so let's just do something to knock him off balance, and then go from there."

"I like that. We'll destabilize him in the safest way we can , and hope he'll find some other resource."

So they did. With the suggestion of the infection control physician and the approval of the cardiologist, they put him on an alternating schedule of cooling him down and heating him up with a thermal blanket, adjusting medication and machine settings along with his own body's adaptive responses to the changes, weaning whenever possible. Like a fisherman alternately giving slack and pulling in tight, these doctors paced along with the patient's own primitive adapting mechanisms, jostling his primal homeostatic systems into gear, until, by some miracle, he pulled out of the downward spiral, stabilized on his own, and recuperated. They helped him access his own healing resources by first knocking him off balance from an artificial stability. What a metaphor for therapy!

How to Recognize and Work
With Feeling-fragments

Like an ancient alchemist assembling the five elements for transformation in the lab, the feeling-centered, body-focused therapist strives to bring feeling-fragments into consciousness, harvest the resulting emotional charge, and set the stage for integration. Feeling-fragments, components of repressed material, cycle and recycle throughout consciousness until they reunite into a whole once more, and then are finally relegated to the realm of neutral memory.

Feeling-fragments are buffered from consciousness by the body's defenses against pain. Pieces of an original painful feeling float around in the nervous system outside the conscious awareness in the form of anxiety, tension, driven thoughts and actions, phobias, and a myriad of other sensations and behaviors. The difference between consciously accessing memory (as in remembering what you had for breakfast yesterday), and being swept into the experience of the re-surfacing of feeling fragments is not a subtle one. You can sense the "I" during conscious access, but not in the case of feeling fragments. Body responses, emotional tones, or meanings (what the person tells himself about an event or experience) can seem out of context, or even extreme, when feeling fragments are unleashed during a therapy session.

Initial listening techniques for the therapist require learning how to identify and distinguish feeling fragments from neutral memories. Other techniques revolve around learning to see the whole picture that is being presented, an exercise that is akin to assembling and aligning the pieces of a puzzle before finally connecting them. Finally, the therapist may need to come up with a highly-charged catalyst that can facilitate the merging of the separated aspects of a feeling into a completed gestalt, or point of wholeness. Attempting to link the pieces solely with "analysis" or "interpretation" tends to derail the integration process, rather than enhancing or quickening it.

A patient who repeatedly employs the same terminology, or even more directly, the same words or phrases to describe unrelated phenomena implies a meaning-fragment. My chiropractor client's wrist injury prevented him from practicing spinal adjustments, or in his terms, "doing what I hold most dear." When he described the collapse of a fruitless business venture, he claimed, "I lost that which was most dear to me." It turned out that this meaning of "losing that which is most dear to me" had resided in a core response when his beloved father died when he was five. Because he was not allowed to go to the funeral and face the finality of death, he had fragmented and spread out his grief that was later manifested in the theme of his current life: "losing what I hold most dear."

When a client repeats phrases, I then repeat those phrases back to him in the same context in order to help create a biological feedback loop into his or her consciousness. I keep the phrase active in the present while "gathering" other feeling fragments and bringing them into the current reality.

When a client repeatedly refers to certain parts of his body through talk or gesture, or indicates chronic physical problems, then I assume I am witnessing a body-response fragment. Sol, 53, with a recent diagnosis of prostate cancer, repeatedly spoke in a penis/sex-related language, calling men "pricks," "dick heads," "cocksuckers," and women were referred to as "ball crushers," and "cockteases." At one point Sol announced, "they'll take your dick if they can." This kind of talk made it obvious to me that we should investigate his teen years. In fact, Sol had had an affair with an aunt, over which he felt both proud and guilty. His father, it turned out, had also had an affair with the same woman, which made Sol feel hurt and angry. And deeply sorry for his mother. So much charge, and no way to process it as a kid!

When a single emotional tone pervades the various areas of a client's life, I think 'emotional fragment.' I believe depression is nothing more than fragmented, disconnected grief. Antidepressants combat the re-emergence of these grief-fragments, thus running counter to the natural integrative processes. When strong emotional fragments of a feeling predominate the feeling-fragment scene, the therapist may decide to defer straight catharsis until other elements creep into consciousness. Many depressed people cry freely and even wallow in sorrow, so facilitating a tearful melt-down is not a cure for depression. Only when the weeping is connected to the true object of grief does the pool of pain actually drain out with some finality. Only when the link to the pain is broken does pain no longer make sense to the system. Paradoxically, this link can only break after first being connected consciously.

"Harvesting" for a missing feeling-fragment can actually be a fun exercise for the therapist, especially when the overall picture becomes clear enough that the fragment can be recognized lurking in the background before the client is even remotely aware that a psychic "soil-tilling" is underway. If the elements of meaning and emotion already reside in the conscious mind, then only body-response remains. A simple shift into body-awareness techniques coaxes the final fragment of consciousness to emerge. If a strong body-response (ie, tingling in hands or feet, tightness in solar plexus, etc.) and a meaning (for example, "I cannot let myself feel," or "they hate me") coexist, then I make a move to elicit emotion. "What is the feeling there?" or, "What does that feel like?" If body-response (i.e, shaking, sweating) and emotion (fear) reside together in the consciousness, then I seek out the meaning that connects them (i.e., "What does this remind you of?" or, "When have you experienced this before?", or even more directly "What does this mean to you?")

It is important to note that these elements want to come together for the sake of biological integration and for gestalt resolution, so the therapist only has to bring them to light and let the natural centropic (or inward, integrative) forces ignite them into wholeness. The closer they come to each other, the more the charge of the moment intensifies, often reflecting an increasing level of resistance. The client will engage in all kinds of distraction gambits at this point, or, if feeling threatened by the imminent shift about to occur in his awareness of pain, he may segue into the more "dangerous" ploy of direct transference onto the therapist. As an East Indian female patient zeroed in on the chauvinistic, hurtful reality of her heretofore revered father, she turned on me with: "I hate you, Andy! How dare you bring this up, how dare you make me feel this way about my father!" That was immediately followed by: "I have never felt as much passion as I do right now. Do you ever engage in discreet liasons with your clients?" She was serious! And had little recognition of the extreme nature of her love-hate projections!

Working with feeling fragments remains the main thrust of therapy because it parallels the body's own integrative processes, and takes into account the natural resistance to pain. If my explanation here sounds simple, then I'm glad. The reality is simple. The artistry of facilitation remains the great challenge because pain is real, and not just a "story." Therapy that deals only with the story and avoids, ignores, or denies the pain factor, does not get to the core.

The Question of Touch in Psychotherapy

In the very early paragraphs of this booklet I went on and on about the essential role touch plays in the normal development of all mammals. Human babies inadequately touched regularly fail to thrive. Increasing tactile stimulation with a woolen under-blanket alone stimulates infant weight gain, decreases fussiness, and improves immune function. Tiffany Field, Ph.D., of the Touch Research Institute of Miami, Florida, has verified via scientific studies what common lore tells us: touch is vital, necessary, and therapeutic. (I bet you, as a bodyworker, are thinking, "DUH! I already know this!" but bear with me, this is just not common understanding in the psych world.) Over fifty hospitals in the United States fund and maintain massage programs, recognizing that such a high-touch approach to patient care yields shorter hospital stays, quicker healing times, overall improved customer satisfaction, and fewer lawsuits (which makes treatment-related touch cost-effective all around).

In mainstream psychology, touch between therapist and client is taboo. Fear says touch will lead either to improper sexual conduct or to a lawsuit, or both. Popular books, movies, and television shows (***The Prince of Tides***, ***Primal Fear***, ***Melrose Place***, etc.) often depict therapists having sex with their clients, with dramatic and dire results. So the message is: avoid touch altogether. Besides, by showing up as the warm, touchy-feelie therapist, you might interfere with, or gloss over, the more difficult aspects of therapy, thereby confusing the transference process. Remaining untouchable insures clean projections. Touch messes that up and confuses boundaries. Touch may also serve to increase or distort the power differential in the already unequal relationship between therapist and client, and influence self-esteem in a destructive way. Touch may therefore be an abuse of power on the therapist's part. Those are the cons.

The pros go like this:
1. Touch increases and quickens the process of transference, and doesn't automatically confuse it. (Transference is already a form of confusion!)
2. Touch provides emotionally-corrective experiences (especially for treating someone who's been physically abused), and reintroduces the idea and reality that touch can be good and part of a healthy relationship.
3. Touch, as a highly charged, non-neutral event, "pushes buttons", by-passes defenses and quickens bodily awareness and feeling-access.
4. More significantly, touch helps mobilize inner resources for healing by stimulating release of thymopoeitan, a hormone which oversees the maturation of T-cells.
5. Touch reinforces boundaries (that's how kids learn them), and does not confuse them.
6. Touch humanizes the difficult process of therapy and adds the necessary element of safety and caring.

The potential to abuse touch in therapy remains, as does the potential to abuse antibiotics during medical treatment, but that doesn't mean they shouldn't be administered wisely and prudently.

What sort of a message does the avoidance of touch really give to a client anyway? That touching is unnatural? And not part of healing? Wrong! Caring, conscious touching injects a powerhouse of life-affirming meanings directly into the bodily neuropeptide network, and greatly facilitates overall healing. Touching is good therapy, and good therapy is touching. Your role as a bodyworker in the bigger picture of helping restore health to your client, is paramount.

My Body-oriented Technique: Centropic Integration

The Beginnings

Centropic Integration (CI) is a body-oriented psychotherapy modality that my friend and colleague, Dr. Camden Clay of Atlanta, Georgia, and I developed in the 1980's out of our own personal growth work, based on our desire to create and be a part of a therapeutic community. We synthesized elements of John Ray's Body ElectronicsTM, Stanislav Grof's Holotropic BreathworkTM, and added our unique form of core-feeling counseling. The essential tools of CI are sustained acupressure point holding, evocative music, and emotional facilitation. We first applied it in a group workshop setting (which evolved out of years of "healing parties" that we hosted) and soon modified it to work in the one-on-one setting.

The Definition

Centropic (in physics, a "movement towards the center") refers to the natural tendency of humans to return to unfinished core experiences or issues for the sake of completing them, and integration refers to the reuniting of disconnected parts. Centropic Integration has as its theoretical foundation the science of psychoneuroimmunology (PNI), which focuses on the biology of memory storage via the neuropeptide system. The goals are to apply those physiological principles to the realm of personal experience, and to use the influence of a group of loving supporters and/or the therapist to bring about desired change in a rapid way. We set out to demonstrate that inner healing does not have to take a long time.

Theoretical Foundations

There is something about humans that is absolutely impressionable. We come into the world with our nervous system wide open, and whatever we encounter, we bring inside and make it a part of ourselves. We naturally absorb the language, cultural norms, customs, and rules of our environment. There is the well-known story of a family that was vacationing in the wilds when their vehicle turned over, and everyone but the infant girl was killed. A pack of wolves found the infant, and a lactating she-wolf adopted the human baby and raised her as her own. (Yes, this sounds like The Jungle Book, but it's a true story!) The little girl grew up with the wolves, scampered around on all fours, ate raw meat, and howled at the moon. As far as she was concerned she was a wolf. Some people discovered her eleven years later, took her back to civilization, and made every effort to remind her of her true nature. The question: was she or was she not a wolf? She was certainly wolf-like in her behavior--a true testament to the extreme impressionability of the human creature--yet in genetics and form, never actually a wolf. (It is interesting to note that the little girl died at the age of thirteen, the natural life span of a wolf in captivity!)

Essence vs. Programming

That story illustrates the difference between, and the potential for, misalignment between essence and programming, which to some degree holds true for each of us. As we grow up encountering and collecting life experiences, we adopt beliefs, cultivate likes and dislikes, and develop a sophisticated self-image and world-view along the way. Unfortunately, during this process, too often our underlying nature of pure, unburdened enthusiasm and happiness is forgotten and covered up. The notion of "learning" becomes the permanent filter through which life is experienced. Eventually, we "mature" to the point where all new input is routed through established memory circuitry, and the past ends up encroaching upon each present experience, by superimposing on it old meanings, associative emotions, and conditioned gut-level body responses. For example: a physically abused child placed in a foster home shirks away from the new genuinely loving touch of her adoptive family, and remains locked into abusive memory pathways. Her former negative conclusions, along with her knee-jerk self-protective body-responses, reinforce a reality long gone.

The past becomes our present. Non-integrated traumatic events or unmet needs tend to be continuously recreated and repeated with new players. It is as if the body gets stuck. I believe a person's current health problems may be a direct outcropping of unfinished emotional and interpersonal business, or in other words, the body's pantomimed response to internalized past programming. What started out as external stressors have been absorbed, becoming internalized stressors, flooding the system with damaging reactions long after the traumatic circumstances have changed.

The seemingly random process I am describing wrecks internal havoc, sometimes via blatantly traumatic events, and sometimes more subtly and incrementally. A sociological study, recording what the average three-year-old in the United States hears from significant adults in a day's time, showed most of the messages to be negative, limiting, and inhibitive. Just as the little wolf-girl grew up with wrong impressions that molded her sense of herself, we, too, absorb a myriad of negative and limiting impressions that occupy our nervous system (in the form of beliefs and mind-maps of reality) and make them the core of our self.

It's In the Body

The science of psychoneuroimmunology states that these negative programs take root in the physical body. In order to make it through overwhelming or painful situations (this can include physical, emotional, or mental pain), people tend to fragment their experience and "hide away" the pieces in the recesses of susceptible tissue and organs, where they are biochemically encoded in their entirety onto neuropeptide molecules. The network of neuropeptides and receptor sites located throughout the soft tissue of the body is what we refer to as "body memory," occurring at both conscious and unconscious levels of awareness. Arthur Janov, author of The Primal Scream, claimed that neurosis, or the splitting up of the whole-brain responses to painful experiences into fragments in order not to feel is one of our unique human survival adaptation methods. Once this splitting (which is basically a numbing of feeling) has occurred, a natural longing for wholeness remains, and it is this longing that mirrors the biologically driven centropic impulse to reintegrate what has been cut off.

After years of witnessing hundreds of clients undergoing natural integrations in the emotionally unfettered environment of our workshops and Centropic Integration sessions, empirical investigation demonstrated to Dr. Clay and me that not only do the memories tagged with a higher emotional charge have a stronger impact on the psyche and the body, but that all experiences stored in memory can be retrieved. Cam's and my belief is simple: consciousness is the cure. Bring these hidden elements of the psyche, especially the heavily emotionally-laden ones, into awareness in the context of a loving, permissive, and embracing setting, and healing results.

The Approach

Centropic Integration as a therapy modality has a three-fold approach. First, a whole-brain, highly-charged desired outcome is instilled into the system, and then the process of accessing and releasing all earlier life-negating programming by encouraging the client to feel repressed pain is inaugurated. The third branch of this method is what we have come to call positive peer pressure, the life-affirming influence of a healing circle, or in the one-on-one setting, the therapist. Personal and individual deep feeling--comprised of meaning, emotion, and body response (reflecting the triune nature of the brain)-- is the key to Centropic Integration and the life-impacting changes it facilitates, and that which separates it from other emotional release-oriented therapies.

Setting the Banks of the River

Before the reservoir of suppressed or unconscious feeling is tapped directly, it is important to set the parameters within which the release is to occur, ensuring that not only will blocked energy be freed, but that the client will be propelled in an empowering direction, shifting from current reality (point A) to where he or she wants to be (point B). A release that occurs without pre-setting the banks of the river too easily ends in a non-productive breakdown, which is unnecessary.

Focus on Feelings

A typical session begins with a face-to-face encounter, with the therapist asking open-ended questions relevant to the client's medical and personal history, and then shifts to focus on emotionally charged material as it arises.

Common questions are: "What are you aware of right now in your body as you tell me about your brother?" or "What is the feeling being expressed in your voice as you mention the hospital?" or "If your heart had a voice right now, what would it say?"

The client's disclosures about the unfulfilled or disappointing aspects of her current reality inevitably reveal underlying existential themes or messages linked to simple core feelings such as grief or loss of innocence. Simple questioning then easily reveals childhood conclusions linked to those feelings which over the years have diminished healthy self-esteem, trust, boundary-setting, and relationships in the adult context, and which of course are no longer relevant. Pain that has been unmasked exposes Point A in all its limitations, and makes letting go easier.

An Aligned Statement of Desired Outcome

The CI facilitator then helps the client to focus on and arrive at an aligned statement of desired and meaningful outcome. For example, "If you could have your life unfold in whatever way you desired, what would it be like?" Some examples of answers are: "I choose to be able to touch others with love without taking on their pain", or, "I choose to know and feel my own heart even if it means feeling pain and disappointment", or, "I choose to consistently stand up for myself even in the face of others' anger and disapproval." Point B choices bring about a sense of possibility of balance and integrity in particularly problematic areas of life.

With both Points A and Point B fully aligned with a meaning, emotion, and body response, the parameters for change (the "banks of the river") are set. Any additional emotional release in the next hands-on phase of the session automatically serves to move the person further along the path to his or her outcome.

Accessing the Memory

Centropic Integration uses sustained hands-on point-holding along acupressure meridian lines to access the body-component of stored fragmented memories. The acupuncture lines of the endocrine system hook directly into the circuitry of the limbic "loop" in the brain where emotional memory is processed. The client lies in a supine position, while appropriate points are determined through a simple system that corresponds to the endocrine glands and various emotional states; we also can assess the client's body response with our hands, seeking points of trigger reaction, or tenderness to touch. Points can be held by one or more participants, with one person taking on the role of facilitator. (Notice how I didn't say "therapist" this time. Cam and I have always felt that this work belongs to the people. A person can be an effective, sensitive facilitator of inner healing without necessarily being a psychotherapist by trade. What they do need is personal experience and some practical training.)

Breathwork and Altered States

The first 60-90 minutes of point-holding are devoted to deep synchronous breathing by client, facilitator, and other participants, accompanied by evocative and emotional music designed to activate and release the abreaction process. Tapping into the long tradition of various cultures that use music to evoke trance states or deep feelings, ranging from tribal drums to a huge pipe organ in a cathedral, this phase of CI elicits both emotion and right-brain, imagery-infused thinking.

Heat, Resistance, and the Body Electric

Just as the electrons in an electric heater generate more heat when we turn the resistor up, acupressure contact points reflect the client's resistance to change: as heat--physical heat! The points get hot to the touch. Resistance, a term often used in psychotherapy to mean the cumulative effect of inner defenses against feeling pain, manifests as a physical phenomenon. All the energy that has been devoted to repression of feeling, when forced to a head, burns. At this time the client may be experiencing images and/or body sensations that either symbolically or directly indicate the spontaneous re-emergence of stored unconscious information that may have to do with non-integrated memories.

The centropic impulse for resolution, coupled with the client's desire for a new outcome, brings the electrical potential at the resistance points up the scale enough to match and finally surpass the resistance. The blocked portions of experience flood forth in emotional catharsis and/or realization, while at the same time biologically integrating the meaning, emotion, and body-response aspects of repressed pain. Point-holding and evocative music thus help "flush out" hidden, peripheral features of experience, making the integrative results of CI dramatic compared to conventional "talk therapies". With conscious catharsis, the Gestalt achieves wholeness once more. (I imagine that if we could monitor the process microscopically we would see the fragmented pieces of the neuropeptides melting together and naturally flowing towards and settling into their proper receptor sites.) The electrical flow of corrected nerve conduction overcomes internalized blocks and surges into any body part where dysfunction had previously resided, often initiating a period of intense burning sensations (the kundalini of Eastern philosophy?), while at the same time the "mind" is flooded with insight about the original issue involved in the trauma or injury, and also about related patterns of behavior. The knowing and understanding of self from this experience is not interpretive, but direct.

The In-filling

The final phase of the session, the "in-filling", which reaches beyond the abundance of insight and the burning inner fire, takes on a spiritual quality hallmarked by serenity and deep body relaxation. Clients report this as a time of integration, a sense of personal victory, and healing, full of recognition and connectedness. The amount of time that has elapsed is about two hours. The session ends with the cooling, pulsing, and releasing of the points, followed by a sense of "afterglow," which can last for hours and sometimes days.

Final Notes

The healing that occurs through Centropic Integration begins with a direct bodily encounter with one's own locked-up pain and resistance to feeling, and ends in renewing daily life with empowering choices and revitalized hope. Unlike the cognitive therapies that effect experience by consciously altering the thinking process, with Centropic Integration cognitive insight happens spontaneously, as a natural outcropping of deeply processed feelings. Follow-up sharing, especially in the intimate group setting of a Centropic Integration workshop, enhances cognitive anchoring. Changes and insights facilitated by a natural integration at the body level endure over time.

"Every muscular contraction contains the history and meaning of its origin."

~Wilhelm Reich

"We are psychological beings and not logical beings."
~Dr. Brad Blanton

***

"Yesterday's truth is today's bullshit."
~Dr. Brad Blanton

***

"Why am I so introspective? I had no place else to go."
~patient

5

Case Studies:
Therapy in Action

Jerry: It All Hurts

Jerry had had a history of migraine headaches since age eleven, for which he had taken medication numerous times. He had noticed that during times of stress the episodes were particularly intense. I was working with him in a group setting where he recounted a life of frustration and lack of fulfillment. He told the group of relationships he had been in and then stated,   "Every time I get into a relationship, I get hurt."

"Close your eyes and say that again," I suggested. He did, deliberately and softly.

"I'm getting a headache," he announced, a slight wince on his face.

"Say it again and let the headache happen," I advised him.

"Every time I get into a relationship, I get hurt."

"Again!"

"Every time I get into a relationship, I get hurt." This time he paused, then biting his lower lip with his upper teeth, and holding his breath, a single tear oozed from his right eye. "To love hurts," he whispered. The tears welled, his energy was wavering, but he was still in control.

"Say that again. That's it right there!"

"To love hurts." This time, the emotions swelled, the control walls started to bend, and more tears funneled down Jerry's cheek.

"Say it again!"

"To love hurts!" he began sobbing. The dam had finally burst, and Jerry's face and body quivered with the letting go.

"Feel that pain, Jerry. Just feel it with no resistance this time, without doing anything about it." The feeling was over the wall, freely flowing now--the body releasing what had been held for a long, long time.

"So what did you choose to do when you realized that 'to love hurts', Jerry?" I demanded.

There was a pause, a slight reflection, and the answer spilled out: "To not love."

"Feel it, Jerry. How does it feel 'to not love'?"

Another full pause and a reply, as if his life were being summed up in two words, "It hurts."

"Feel it, Jerry. That's the existential corner you've painted yourself into. Just feel it and be with it."

In a flash, a life-strategy based on avoiding pain had been revealed. The core belief stood exposed: to love hurts; to not love hurts. Opposing forces held within the body, leaving Jerry in the middle zone of neither loving nor not-loving. No feeling. Jerry, working as an accountant, had "lived in his head" for years. Carrying this unresolved dilemma had created the prodigious amount of pressure inside his head.

"So, Jerry, what's your new choice here? Understand--there's pain at either end, and let's face it, avoiding the pain didn't work." The room was thick with a delicious silence as the whole group sat poised for his answer...

"I choose to love," Jerry whispered, with a peace and resolve that shone on his wet cheeks, "even if there is pain." He sighed. Everyone else in the room sighed. It was sweet and true. Jerry had made a good life-affirming choice for himself, and we could see that it was…well, livable.

Jerry now sat charged with the same emotional energy that had fed the fruitless strategy of avoiding pain. Once the body response had lined up with the new choice, it became part of the domain of the subconscious. No litany of affirmations would be necessary to maintain the vitality around that choice. A new path of least resistance had been born within his being.

"How's your headache?" I asked.

"What headache?"

Phase two of Jerry's session involved some gentle acupressure point-holding, along with mellow music, to help him rest in the newfound peace of a life-strategy that suited him. In follow-up appointments, Jerry reported a marked decrease in the migraines, both in intensity and frequency. Migraine headaches were now experienced more as red flag indicators around his issue of choosing to love vs. choosing to not feel pain, and when he felt one was imminent, he knew how to ward it off.

Jona: Hope Does a Body Good

Jona had been struggling with myeloma for ten months, and during his illness, he had been through many ups and downs. One day he and I discussed hope.

"I'm afraid to feel hope and then have what I'm doing not work, because I'm setting myself up for disappointment. If I don't hope so much, I won't feel as hurt if it doesn't work out."

"You mean, the higher you fly, the harder you can crash?" I asked.

"Right."

"What does hope feel like?"

"Like making a plan and being able to carry it out."

"That's not a feeling, Jona. That's a definition based on the future. And if you define hope that way, nothing will change. What does hope feel like?"

"Like the good feeling I get when I've made a plan and carried it out."

"That's a feeling based on the past---having carried something out. Close your eyes, Jona. What specifically does hope feel like?"

"A lightness in my chest, and an open feeling in my head."

"Now feel it and recognize it. This is hope in the present---independent of the future and the past. This is yours now. There is no such thing as 'false hope,' because hope exists in the present."

"Mmmmm. Thanks, I accept that!"

Lydia: I'm Not Supposed to Be Here

'I'm not supposed to be here. This is where people die. I can't die here. I need treatment--the strongest chemo and radiation possible. I want to live. I have to see my grandchildren grow up!" Lydia lay in her bed at hospice, emaciated except for swollen legs and abdomen. Her breathing labored, she poured out her concerns to me.

"Look what I've done to myself! I've smoked for over forty years and have destroyed this beautiful temple God has given me, and now I've got to fight!"

"Isn't it too late?" I asked.

"No, I can't believe that! How can I be at peace knowing what I've done? I must fight so I'll know that I did all I could to save my body. Then I can be at peace."

"Do you think you could ever forgive yourself?" I questioned.

"Maybe, if I fight with all I've got, and get the strongest treatment there is..."

"What about forgiving yourself first?"

"No, that's not possible. If I did that, I'd lose my motivation. I'd just give up."

A long pause followed and we sat in silence together, Lydia's inner turmoil still apparent in her wrinkled brow and restlessness.

"Are you hurting?" I asked.

"Badly. I can't stand it, but I need to fight this thing."

"Lydia, have you ever done something that inadvertently hurt someone else?"

"Yes, why?"

"Who did you hurt?"

"My son."

"How did that feel to you?"

"Oh, horrible, when I realized what I had done. I felt terrible about it."

"Then what happened?"

"He was mad at first, and then he forgave me when he saw how sorry I was." Her eyes moistened with the memory.

"And how did that moment feel to you?"

"Just wonderful. Actually, bittersweet. Even though I hurt him, and that was for real, he still loved me."

"What did that feel like in your body in that moment?"

"It was warm, and I relaxed a lot. We cried together and hugged. It was very warm." A tear leaked out and down Lydia's cheek.

"Lydia, that's the feeling forgiveness creates. It is a good and a powerful healing thing to do for yourself. Couldn"t you find it in your heart to forgive yourself now? You certainly are sorry for what you've done, right?"

"Oh, yes."

"And you want to do what is best for your body now, right?"

"Right. But what about the will to fight?" she demanded, already relaxing her shoulders and slowing her breath.

"What about: 'forgive first, then fight like hell?' You've already done so many bad things for your body, isn't it time to do something good for it now?"

"Yes, you have a point. 'Forgive now, and fight like hell too.' Yes, that feels very good." She lay back, mulling over a new approach.

"And think about it, Lydia, if you do such strong chemo and radiation, you might not even be up to forgiving yourself after."

"True. I can't put that off. I am sorry for what I've done." She glanced up, fixed her concentrated gaze on mine, and the tension melted from her face. "Thank you," she whispered.

Client Stories
Life With Feeling Makes Sense

Once deep feelings surface in therapy, and the integrative forces of the body/mind system successfuly yield closure to painful imprints, life begins to make sense. Patterns of unconscious behavior, both large and small, suddenly stand out clearly, and you might think: "How could I have been so blind?"

The following are patients' commentaries on their therapy in light of their deep inner work. Notice the sense of being extricated from tightly woven dramas---a liberation that comes not just from knowing about the family or personal history involved, but from knowing the history as it flows forth from feeling. Notice also how repressing feeling at different developmental levels of childhood results in different degrees of suffering. The rule of thumb in this regard: "the earlier the repression, the more widespread the damage to the psyche".

The addage: "change your mind and change your life" contains great wisdom. When your worldview is altered, so is your world. A person riddled with repression inevitably carries a world riddled with struggle. True organismic change comes about by reaching and emptying the recesses of repressed feeling at levels below the conscious mind which then undoes warped higher levels of thought and belief that came about to mask pain. Feeling feelings clears the mind, and unclutters the world.

Heinrich: Too Much Pain

"I can only begin to tell you the many levels of insight reliving this one scene from my infancy has brought me. I'm not talking "insight" as in intellectual saavy, either. Not only do I now know what's made me feel bad much of my life, I no longer feel driven to ever go there again. It even feels strange to talk about the whole thing now, because it's finally where it belongs--my past!

After many therapy sessions of crying, it finally seemed like I was cried out. I lay on the carpet feeling empty, but not in the good sense. I've learned in therapy to go with my feleings, and sink into them, but this one felt so vague, very much body-sensation-oriented. So I just breathed into it, and before long I entered what's like a 3-D movie. I felt the presence of big people, and feelings of excitement, somehow shrouded with religiousness. It reminded me of of the vibe in the Temple where I was Bar-Mitzvahed.

I felt myself very little, cradled in large hands. I felt the total-body relaxed sense of trust as my arms and thighs were strapped to the table top. I heard the deep chanting of a man's voice, and felt swells of pride and tears from my mother sitting nearby. And then the horrible pain! The bearded man had grabbed my penis, swabbed it with something very cold, and then cut into me! I tightened every muscle and strained as my penis burned with agonizing hurt. I couldn't cry or scream hard enough to keep the throbbing ache away. My system went into shock, physically, emotionally, and spiritually, if you will. Waves of pain washed over me. Thoughts like: "I can never feel good again" and "Nobody knows my pain" crashed through my little brain, and my heart contracted to remove me from this horrible place. How could I ever relax in the presence of others again?

"Human contact means unpredictable senseless pain" has been my unspoken motto my whole life, with numerous reinforcements along the way.

I experienced something in that moment of re-living, that I've noticed in other therapy sessions too: inner connections. Other scenes throughout my life, even up to adult life, that I knew were directly connected to this single original scene flashed into my consciousness. I recognized them as not related, but the same as. You could call it "making sense" if you wanted to. I got it, because my body got it.

For me, I flashed on numerous times right after sex with my girl-friends, I'd have that same horrible empty feeling along with "nobody knows my pain". I always thought I was weird like that. I flashed on times people I was close with had gotten angry at me, and how I always seemed to go into "mini-shock" over it, and frequently would say: "That came out of nowhere". Any little shocks resonated that big shock response still locked within me.

I've reflected on my circumcision experience many times since that session. How tragic that we humans can inflict pain so unconsciously that we even celebrate it with feelings like pride or patriotism. How can we be so oblivious to the pain of others? I think about how we wage war, and rationalize all the misery that comes with it. I have a whole different view about senseless pain now that I've felt what it's like to be the innocent object of it.

6

Suggested Reading:
Book Reviews

In no particular order:

1. *The Power of the Mind to Heal*, by Joan Borysenko, PhD & Miroslav Borysenko, PhD. Hay House, Inc., Carson, California, 1994.

Two powerhouse medical scientists pull together a very humanistic documentation of the healing power of the mind from such diverse areas as medical case studies, near death experiences, and ancient Buddhist scriptures. They intersperce their book with little "exercises" to make the didactic material real in the moment. The Borysenko's, although very hightly professionally credentialed, are far from "stuffy intellectuals", and serve up a very pallitable fare in this ecclectic work.

2. *Anatomy of an Illness*, by Normin Cousins. Bantam Books. New York, New York, 1979.

This is the classic work of the Father of the modern Mind/ Body movement, and remains as inspiring and valid as ever. Norman Cousins healed himself of a degenerative autoimmune condition through the power of laughter, and formulated a viable mind/body paradigm in the process.

3. *Bodymind*, by Ken Dychtwald. GP Putnam's Sons, New York, New York. 1977.

Presents a conceptual "map" of the body areas and what aspects of personality or emotion can be read in them. Synthesizes the work of Reich, Feldenkrais, and Fritz Perls to suggest body-oriented ways of facilitating therapy and personal development. The feel of this book is dated to the Human Potential Movement of the Sixties and Seventies.

4. *Your Body Speaks Its Mind*, by Stanley Keleman. Center Press, Berkeley, California, 1975.

What is the body's perspective on itself, the existence of others, its being in the world? This is not only the goal of Keleman's book, it is also its style: a stream-of-consciousness, on-going body metaphor that reads like the diary of an aboriginal native in downtown Manhattan. Kelemen's point, made from within his Reichian/bioenergetics background, is that the body is in fact aboriginal, meaning it was there first. He speaks of the human being as primarily "embodied", yet in a way that stands far afield from Skinner's behavioristic view as well as from the Romantic perspective of the body as "Primitive Child". The body, says Keleman, is a matter of "embodied consciousness", which speaks of an innate intelligence, sensitivity, and even relatedness--a natural "mind", if you will, that is more unity-oriented than divisive, more connected than separate. Thus the way to "read" or reach the mind is through the embodied messages of the body. Keleman, primarily a psychotherapist rather than a bodyworker, focuses on soma to reach psyche.

This book follows an unrelenting course in its body-as-metaphor style, but basically it's a good trip.

5. *The Healing Brain: Breakthrough Discoveries About How the Brain Keeps Us Healthy*, by Robert Ornstein and David Sobel. Simon and Schuster, New York, New York, 1987.

I'm not sure why this isn't an exciting book. The authors present the basic psychoneuroimmunology information in a very readable fashion, and even have funny chapter titles like, *"Pressure: Social and Blood"*, or *"Great Expectations: On the Reduction of Warts and the Enlargement of Breasts"*, or *"Friends Can Be Good Medicine"*. Brain research studies described from first-hand experience along with all the other science presented in the book are flawless and plentiful. All the right ingredients are present. The book is decently organized, notated, and indexed. It's just not inspiring. I give it a "B-".

6. *The Healer Within: the New Medicine of Mind and Body*, by Steven Locke, MD, and Douglas Colligan. New American Library, New York, New York, 1986.

I continue to tap the vast resources of this book, chock full of great "hard science" about the mind-body connection and fanciful story-telling. The depths of linkage between physical science at the level of cellular activity and the experiential level of experience makes for a noble effort indeed! Like looking at the vast array of stars at night with textbook in hand, we are still primarily left with a sense of mystery and awe. Dr. Locke's explanations of immune function and its response to various emotional stimulii, seem to speak the language of science, but remain rooted in this heartland of wonder. Also contains a full 50 pages of appendices, networking resources, glossary, and index.

7-11. *The Primal Revolution*; Simon & Shuster; New York, New York;

1972.

Primal Man: the New Consciousness; Thomas Y. Crowell Co.;New York, New York;1975.

Imprints: the Life-long Effects of the Birth Experience; Coward-McCann, Inc.; New YOrk, New York, 1983.

The New Primal Scream: Primal Therapy 20 Years On; Enterprise Publishing, Inc.; Wilmington, Delaware; 1991.

Why You Get Sick; How You Get Well; Dove Books; West Hollywood, California; 1996. All by Dr. Arthur Janov.

Let me sing the praises of Dr. Janov and the significance of his work in bringing deep feeling therapy to the forefront of psychological inquiry. I've been following his career for over thirty-five years now. He single-handedly spearheaded the movement in therapy in the early Seventies away from the prevalent strict rational and behavioral approaches, and into the depths of the Unconscious, and has since systematically worked to quantify his findings with rigorous scientific research. Janov has done more to justify and verify the humanistic, feeling approach to wellness than even Carl Rogers, the creator of Client-Centered Therapy, who also insisted on studious research and follow-through in his work.

Janov has taken the brilliance of the Freudian notion that illness results from supressed childhood trauma, and married it with the latest in neurobiological discovery, to develope a practical methodology (Primal Therapy) for not only understanding the underlying causes of diseases, but also for getting well.

Janov is the only one of merit in the field of psychology who has had the balls to speak of cure when it comes to mental illness. His approach and results are convincing and compelling.

12 & 13. *Super Immunity*; by Dr. Paul Pearsall; Ballentine Books; New York, New York; 1987. and *The Heart's Code: Tapping the Wisdom and Power of Our Heart Energy*; by Paul Pearsall; Broadway Books; New York, New York; 1998.

Dr. Pearsall bases his definition of super immunity ("the capacity to think and feel in ways that can protect us from disease,") on the Rational-Emotive Therapy (RET) premise that thought precedes behavior determines feelings. He then makes an elaborate case that this chain of command, with thought at its front, influences health. "Immune cells behave as confidently and effectively as the thinker in which the cells circulate," he states.

He goes on to introduce the concept of Hot and Cold personality traits (loosely drawn from Oriental Medicine) to provide a structure within which to facilitate the inner harmony of opposites necessary to bring about health. The restoration of immune function can be brought about through a peaceful focus on balance, and does not require more aggressively-based PACMAN-type imagery work a la the Simontons, he maintains.

Hot and Cold aside, the importance of this book, in my opinion, lies in its recognition of happiness as central to wellness, and unhappiness as a prelude to disease--hinting at the central role of the heart in the disease and healing process.

A great seguay to Dr. Pearsall's latest book, *The Heart's Code*, in which he finally makes the leap beyond his brain's desperate attempts to make way for the heart, and steps into the realm of the heart itself. Enough of Hot and Cold already!

In *The Heart's Code*, Dr. Pearsall continues his eloquent infusion of good science into matters of heart and mind. This book reads like a revelation, in which Dr. Pearsall orchestrates the latest findings in the cellular world of neurotransmitters, peptides, and receptors to harmonize with his own inner vision and experience of the energy and importance of the heart in healing. His personal growth from Super Immunity days shows dramatically, like the difference between a stock market report and a poetry reading.

14. *The Relaxation Response*; by Dr. Herbert Benson; William Morrow; New York, New York; 1975.

A classic from 1975 in which Dr. Benson makes a compelling case for meditation as an antidote to stress. He shows evidence via oxygen consumption tests, brainwave activity, and blood lactate levels (associated with anxiety) that meditation is more beneficial than sleep.

His book marks the first time, I believe, that the term "altered states of consciousness" is presented in medical literature, as something not only innate to human capacity, but also something beneficial. I like how Dr. Benson presents this healthy alteration of consciousness as an outcropping from what is primarily a body response. Which makes Dr. Benson an important cohort in the mind-body movement.

15. *The Joy of Feeling: Bodymind Acupressure*; by Iona M. Teeguarden; Japan Publications, Inc.; New York, New York; 1984.

Seeing as how I also incorporate acupressure into my psychotherapy work, how could I not buy a book with a title like this? I'm curious whenever I discover a therapist who blends bodywork with inner work.

Teeguarden's premise of: "unblock the body, unlock the psyche" goes hand in hand with her faith in a natural unfolding of health from the inside out, lifting any external restrictions or impositions on the feeling life, such as "should's" or "have-to's" or "nice". She deals with the psychological and physical armoring of the person by focusing on unblocking emotions.

Most of this book intricately weaves an Oriental Medicine approach with all its yin-yang, hot-cold, energy-flow terminology into a neo-Reichian approach to psychotherapy via many case studies. The mythological style with which she relates organ systems to feelings, highlights, in my opinion, the right-brain way body-mind reality really works. Unless you're interested in the specific mappings of Oriental medicine, though, this book is not for you.

16. *Depression and the Body: the Biological Basis of Faith and Reality*; by Alexander Lowen; Penguin Books; New York, New York; 1972.

This book presents a view and treatment of depression via Bioenergetics, Lowen's body-oriented psychotherapy off-shoot of Wilhelm Reich's work. Because depression stands as a symptom of a severance with reality, the aim of treatment is to reconnect with reality. But which beliefs or perceptions are "real"? The only common and abiding reality is bodily reality. Therefore mental illness as distinct from bodily reality is an illusion. The marriage of body and mind happen through emotion. Emotional illness (rather than "mental" illness) results when emotions don't move, and remain frozen within the body. Therefore, reconnecting with reality means getting in touch with and moving emotion.

A depressed person is someone unable to respond to life, like a violin with flaccid strings. Tighten the strings and the instrument comes alive with a renewed ability to respond. Help a person reconnect with emotion at a bodily level, and he's no longer depressed.

Lowen grounds his treatments in the body, using bioengergetic techniques to focus on the movement of emotion. This might involve pressing the feet into the handle of a tennis racket until they hurt as a way of reawakening feeling in a numbed-out area. It might involve swinging arms and pounding pillows till anger flows. Or reaching with arms outstretched for love and pleasure until grief flows forth in tears and sobs. Only when the past gets mechanically unlocked from the body can the entire system become un-depressed and return to the naturally joyous reality of engaging the world with biological pleasure. Lowen defines "faith" is that quality of experience that associates contact with the world with pleasure and satisfaction, and makes reaching out for it an act of positive expectation.

The   premise of Bioenergetics that the body is the person, absolutely radicalizes the treatment, and makes this book fascinating.

17. **Frogs Into Princes**; by Richard Bandler and John Grinder; Real People Press; Moab, Utah; 1985.

Using the fact that the subconscious mind makes no distinction between inner and outer realities and is thereby open to suggestions, Neurolinguistic Programming™ (NLP) sets about facilitating life changes directly and quickly. Bandler and Grinder distilled out of their astute evaluation and analysis of the interactive work of great therapists such as Fritz Perls, Milton Erikson, and Virginia Satir, an elegant methodology for accessing and effecting the inner world of the subconscious. This book introduces the notion of adjusting to the client's communication style via accessing cues, anchoring and reframing techniques. Although I value their work and intent, and agree that transformation doesn't have to take a long time, I believe they short-change the role of emotions in the process.

18. **The Psychobiology of Mind Body Healing: New Concepts of Therapeutic Hypnosis**; by Ernest L. Rossi, Ph.D.; W.W Norton & Co., Inc.; New York, New York; 1986.

Talk about scholarly and sophisticated! Listen to this: *"Wondering absent-mindedly about a personal problem during the comfort of a psycho-biological ultradian rest period is a natural way of accessing and spontaneously reframing and resolving the state-bound encoding of the problem."* So many new concepts! Such consciousness about the smallest of cues from the client! Such subtle interventions!

Rossi not only outlines his own hypnotherapic approach to therapy, giving rationale in the most sophisticated of scientific understandings, he also includes for the reader a comprehensive history of the development of neurobiology that lead up to his understanding and use of it.

Rossi played right-hand man to master practioner, Milton Erikson, for years, and in this work proves himself masterful in his own right. If you don't mind tackling sentences like the italicized one above, and are willing to learn the specific lingo involved, this book is supreme in its field.

19. **Molecules of Emotion: Why You Feel the Way You Feel;** by Candace Pert, Ph.D.; Scribner; New York, New York; 1997.

Candace Pert wins the MVP award in her league of mind/body inquiry. In this book she not only outlines in easy lay terminology, the latest scientific understanding of the neuropeptide system as carrier of emotional messages throughout the body, but also provides a very personal history of key discoveries in the field. Lord knows, she was there! She also paints a macabre picture of scientific politics involved in the development of her Peptide T treatment for AIDS.

Meeting Ms. Pert in 1996 absolutely confirmed my status as her fan. If you get to hear her lecture, go for it.

20. *Primal Connections: How Our Experiences From Conception to Birth Influence Our Emotions*, Behavior, and Health; by Elizabeth Noble; Fireside Book; New York, New York; 1993.

This book actually focuses on accessing and making conscious, imprints from pre-natal times. Noble believes that problems in the present remain rooted in the system as long as they lay shrouded in a cloud of amnesia surrounding original trauma. Bodily sensations from conception to birth build the foundation of feelings, relationship styles, and sense of self, and therefore have a primary unconscious effect on our present lives.

Noble highlights the mythological, almost cosmic, nature of perinatal imagery and thought, and spells out the sort of open-ended therapeutic environment required to facilitate inner access at these levels of awareness. Expect anything! The pre-birth world has its own reality and rules! Primal Connections brims over with case studies and enough actual therapy scenerios to paint a credible picture of an incredible reality.

21. *Kids Learn From the Inside Out: How to Enhance the Human Matrix*; by Shirley L. Randolph, MA, PT, and Margot C. Heiniger, MA, OTR; Legendary Publishing Company; Boise, Idaho; 1994.

All problems stem from missed or thwarted stages of development. Therefore, treatment for conditions like ADD, emotional disturbance, and, well, just about everything, relies on methods to re-do those retarded elements of nervous system functioning.

The authors ellucidate normal human development in the formative years of childhood, showing how growth truly begins from inner impulses, and progresses outward into contact functions. They point out the key areas where this process can be derailed, and offer the basic tools to remedy and facilitate the nervous system getting back on track. It comes down to three basic treatments: skin brushing, cross-crawl repatterning, and corrective re-parenting. Too simple? Maybe that basic.

22. *At the Speed of Life: A New Approach to Personal Change Through Body-Centered Therapy*; by Gay Hendricks, Ph.D, and Kathlyn Hendricks, Ph.D.; Bantam Books; New York, New York; 1993.

"Essence seeks to get us to the light, but persona seeks only to get us through the night." Thus do the authors make the distinction between the authentic and less-than-authentic identities we embody at different times. They say body-centered therapy solves the central split between thinking and feeling by facilitating a direct reconnection with bodily reality.

They offer the five fundamental principles behind body-centered therapy: Presencing ("be with it"), Magnification ("feel it more"), Breathing ("breathe into it"), Moving ("let your body express itself"), and Communication ("tell the truth"), and numerous techniques to facilitate them.

I love the Hendricks' working definitions of the truth ("something you can't argue about") and love ("being happy in the same space as someone or something else"). Kudos to the Hendricks' for making their art so reachable and teachable.

23. *A General Theory of Love*; by Thomas Lewis, M.D., Fari Amini, M.D., and Richard Lannon, M.D.; Random House; New York; 2000.

Reading *A General Theory of Love* is like watching a Discovery Channel special on animal intelligence while sipping champagne in a hot tub: soothing and sensual, insightful and affirming--all the while maintaining a strong scientific edge.

The authors, three psychiatrists, wax poetic in their earnest investigation into the origin, function, and even the future of love. Taking our current understanding of the brain to its zenith, they espouse a unifying theory to explain how love truly sits at the center of what it means to be a human.

Beginning with a novel concept they call limbic resonance to explain our innate capacity as mammals to perceive the inner reality of others, they proceed to solidify their case for the evolutionary triumph of feelings, and ultimately of love itself.

This book overflows with magic, both in fluency of style and in its mixture of hard fact and poetic vision. To receive scientific verification of the heart's pivotal place in nature's design, validates our humanness in a way that relaxes and energizes, and fills the reader with, OK, I'll say it: divinity.

24. *The Betrayal of the Body*, by Alexander Lowen; Macmillan Publishing Company; New York; 1969.

Although this book is dated in its terminology, the whole notion of mental illness as rooted in bodily experience and subject to uprooting and healing through psycho-physical interventions is timely and relevant to bodyworkers.

Lowen's premise is that the feeling of identity arises from a feeling of contact with the body. In schizophrenia, for instance, there is such a complete loss of body contact to such an extent that the schizophrenic not only doesn't know who he is, he is out of touch with reality. "Since his ego is not identified with his body, and does not perceive it in an alive way, he feels unrelated to the world and to people." Loss of touch with the body results in loss of touch with reality. Personal identity has substance only insofar as it is based on the reality of bodily feeling.

Lowen's bioenergetics treatments zero in on helping the client reconnect with bodily relaity through basic grounding and emotionally expressive exercises.

25. *Touch Therapy,* by Helen Colton; Kensington Publishing Corporation; New York; 1985.

Colton's book is neither scientific nor technique oriented. It offers no theory or methods. It is more a sensitive social commentary on the need and lack of touch in our everyday lives.

Originally published under the title of "*The Gift of Touch*" in 1983, Colton's message is still relevant and inspiring.

26. *The Body Remembers: The Psychophysiology of Trauma and Trauma Treatment,* by Babette Rothschild; W.W. Norton & Company; New York; 2000.

Although this is a book for trauma therapists, I include it here because Ms. Rothschild champions the role of the body in trauma treatment and reaches out for the integration of the verbal and somatic approaches. And let's face it: of all the things that surface for a client during a bodywork session, traumatic memories are high on the list.

She divides her book into two sections: Theory, and Practice, and presents all sorts of humble caveats as to the full objectivity of the theories presented, and offers her treatment methods under a similar context of "these are just guidelines, listen to your wisdom and intuition". I respect her a lot for that.

In the Theory section, Rothschild outlines the latest findings in neurobiology about the autonomic nervous system (ANS), and how its two branches, the sympathetic and the parasympathetic, operate. She goes on to describe the ANS interface with the two other brain structures, the hippocampus and the amygdila, in the body's response to trauma. In essence, trauma, she says, gets imprinted in the body when the raw, emotional implicit memory of the amygdila dominates over the explicit, conscious memory of the time-line producing hippocampus.

With all that theory under our belts, we can then precede to the Practice section, which is predicated on the single principle: that a therapist can accelerate or decelerate the ANS excitation response of a traumatized patient and somehow artfully help them weave their unconscious impressions into conscious control. Safety is her watchword, and she emphasizes it so much, some might say she drives the therapy vehicle with her foot on the brake pedal. But I respect her for her caution, and not wanting to either re-traumatize her patients or even throw them into over-whelm. She also emphasizes how the relationship between therapist and client can and ought to be the main source of safety and healthy contain-ment.

Although a little heady, this book stands as a good chal-lenging read for the bodyworker who wants to know how ef-fective trauma therapists look at the body's role in healing.

27. *The Body in Recovery: Somatic Psychotherapy and the Self*, by John P. Conger; Frog, Ltd.; Berkeley, California; 1994.

"The transference evoked by touch and postion are at the heart of a psychological body therapy." Therapists not only evoke feelings in their clients through physical contact but also via how and where they position themselves spacially in relation to the client. This, he says, is the main tool of touch therapy, and its innate power.

By weilding one's own bodymind with authentic, caring presence, the therapist confronts the client at a somatic level, and tweaks into awareness, all the facets of repressed material, character armoring, and unexpressed emotion.

Conger uses the orgone model of Wilhelm Reich, and Lowen's bioenergetic techniques, including hitting, kicking, and lying prone with hours of deep breathing, to elaborate on that vigorous energy exchange between practitioner and client at the foundation of his body psychotherapy. His work is rooted in Jung's Depth Psychology, but he often throws his theoretic map out the window to favor basic body movement techniques that foster grounding and somatic expression. Intense is the word. But because he speaks such words of honoring of his client's integrity, I'd work with him in a heartbeat. I recommend his book to bodyworkers who want to see a holistic body-centered psychotherapist in action, so don't let the specialized Reichian focus deter you.

28. *The Body Electric: Electromagnetism and the Foundation of Life*, by Robert O. Becker, MD., and Gary Selden; William Morrow Publishing; New York; 1985.

OK, I've picked another oldie to review and recommend. But this one really is a classic in the woo-woo mind/body department. The authors, from their observations of the regenerative powers of lizards to re-grow their tails, hypothesized that regeneration of tissue must somehow be an innate ability of all animals and perhaps only needs some sort of external nudge to make it a reality. The nudge, they say, is electricity.

Using all sorts of experiments with mammals and a whole range of electrical stimulation around injuries and tumors, they prove that electricity, both in presence and absence, alters the healing process. OK, so far it's fascinating enough.

They then take their findings to the next level: tapping in to the electricity generated by one's own nervous system, epsecially in the form of thoughts and feelings.

I like how this gives scientific validity to such a "paranormal" notion: that the body is electric by nature, needs adequate electrical stimulation, and that both external and internal sources of the right charge can be restorative and curative. Awesome! Every bodyworker sings the body electric!

TWO OTHER RESOURCES:

1. For the definitive word on meditation/getting in touch inside, contact Words of Peace Global at www.wordsofpeace.org

2. For the definitive word on raw, living food cuisine, alternative healing, and healthy spa living, contact the Hippocrates Health Institute at 1443 Palmdale Ct., West Palm Beach, Florida 33411, or call (561) 471-8876, or visit www.hippocratesinst.org

Post Script

As a psychotherapist I know that it takes a lot to shift old patterns of behavior, to change years of habitual thinking, to lighten the burden of long-held beliefs, to free a person from the prison of their own limitations and assumptions. I know that it takes more than gradual inevitable evolution to bring about the healing changes people yearn for. It often takes revolution, especially to override the mind/body's prime directive to avoid pain.

That's where touch comes in. Touch not only triggers imprinted pain to rise to the surface of consciousness, but it elicits, like nothing else, the urge to feel good, and keep feeling good. Touch awakens the deepest stirrings for our true human destiny: to be simple, feeling, connected beings, comfortable in our own skin.

At the Hippocrates Health Institute, in West Palm Beach, Florida, I work with acupuncturists, bodyworkers, sound therapists, colon therapists, and aestheticians, and we refer clients to each other as the need warrants. We share our expertise with each other and collaborate.

I wrote this book in the spirit of team-building, to empower bodyworkers, so they may know how to recognize pending, impending, and current emotionally integrative experiences in their clients, and know whether and when to refer them for further inner work. So they may grow not only in vocabulary, but in wisdom with their awesome knowledge of the power of touch.

"Connection normalizes every aspect of our being."
~Arthur Janov

About Andy Bernay-Roman

Andy Bernay-Roman, Licensed Mental Health Counselor (LMHC), Nationally Certified Counselor (NCC), MS, RN, LMT, works in his private psychotherapy practice in South Florida, and lives with his therapist/artist wife, Lynne, and their cat, Willa. Their son, Eli, lives in Washington, DC, and their daughter, Kaia, lives with her husband, Dan, and their two daughters, Kira and Nava, in Santa Cruz, California.

Andy was a 1995 nominee for the Norman Cousins Award and the Rosalyn Carter Caregiver Award.

Andy has also served since 1990 as mind/body psychotherapist at the world-renowned Hippocrates Health Institute in West Palm Beach, Florida, where he treats individuals, couples, and families, and also facilitates the on-going Healing Circle.

Feedback and Contact

Andy welcomes your feedback. You can contact him at : **andy@deepfeeling.com** or at (561)471-5867.

Ordering More Books

If you'd like to order more copies of *Deep Feeling, Deep Healing, Mind/Body Wisdom for Bodyworkers* you can do so online at www.deepfeeling.com/book.html or from Amazon.com.

Also, look into Andy's "original" *Deep Feeling, Deep Healing: The Heart, Mind, and Soul of Getting Well,* in English, French and Russian!

7155544R00063

Printed in Great Britain
by Amazon.co.uk, Ltd.,
Marston Gate.